CBAC

MODULAR BIOLOGY

Units BI1 & BI2

Gareth Rowlands

AS LEVEL

WJEC AS Level Modular Biology
Units BI 1 & BI 2

Published by the Welsh Joint Education Committee
245 Western Avenue, Cardiff CF5 2YX

First published 2001

Printed by Hackman Printers Ltd
Clydach Vale, Tonypandy, Rhondda, CF40 2XX

ISBN: 1 86085 468 0

Introduction

Students are often uncertain as to what is required of them in preparation for the exams

This booklet:
- ✓ provides guidance for students specifically studying WJEC AS Biology.
- ✓ is a study guide and **you should build on the information provided by using a text book** and **your lesson notes**.
- ✓ gives some indication of the main points to be noted.
- ✓ gives some guide as to the depth of treatment required.

An active role in your studies

- • In order to revise effectively it is important to take an **active role** in the process. Passive reading through your notes has limited value. The guide suggests '**Action points**' where you:
- ✓ draw labelled diagrams.
- ✓ draw graphs.
- ✓ analyse result tables.
- ✓ highlight key terms and provide definitions.
- ✓ construct comparison tables.
- ✓ describe processes using flowcharts/flow diagrams.
- • This does not mean that these activities are the only ones that you should carry out in preparation for an exam. They are merely suggestions. There may, for example, be a number of other drawings that you should consider.

Revision hints

Examiners are aware that candidates are often not able to effectively show the examiner what they know.
To overcome this problem it is necessary to:
- ✓ devise a structured **revision programme**. Revise regularly - repetition is an important tool in learning and in preparing for exams. Revise each topic as soon as it is completed. Success is achieved through consistent work rather than attempting to commit everything to memory at the last minute.
- ✓ **understand basic principles** e.g. by learning definitions.
- ✓ **revise all topics**. Each unit will contain a number of structured questions with one essay question. It is not a good idea to work out which topics are 'going to come up'. Examiners take great care that the questions cover every topic.
- ✓ produce **annotated diagrams** – these are a good way of revising!
- ✓ familiarise yourself with **past exam questions**.
- ✓ **express yourself clearly and concisely** -frequently students, who know a reasonable amount of biology, don't do themselves justice in an exam because of their poor exam technique. Much of this is to do with the problem of language. It can make the difference between a good grade and an average grade. You need to be able to read, interpret, memorise, understand and convey information concisely in order to answer exam questions successfully.
- ✓ understand the **key words** that are used in exam questions.

It is hoped that the guide may prove of real value to the student.
The author is a chief examiner for the WJEC and has written a further revision guide for the new specification 2001 together with a question book.

Revision express "A - level study guide Biology" (Pearson Education)
Revision express "AS Fast-track Biology" (Pearson Education)

Both publications complement the information in this booklet and provide an extension to the activities and information outlined here. This booklet, which emphasises the WJEC specific material, is largely, though not exclusively, based on the study guide.

(Discounted Revision Express publications are available direct from Pearson Education, Edinburgh Gate, Harlow, Essex CM20 2JE)

Gareth Rowlands, February 2001

Websites

http://ncbe.reading.ac.uk.

http://vector.cshl.org

http://www.newscientist.com/nsplus/insight/gmworld/gmfood.html

http://jic.bbsrc.ac.uk/exhibitions/bio-future/index.htm

http://www.greenpeace.org.uk

http://www.wildlifetrust.org.uk

www.indiana.edu/~cheminfo/09-16.html

www.biology.arizona.edu

www.wsuonline.weber.edu/course.botany.130/unit1_la.htm

www.sturgeon.ab.ca/rw/Pyramids/ecopyra.html

www.revision-express.com

www.wjec.co.uk

1.1 Biological compounds

Certain molecules have particular functions in living organisms. These functions depend on the properties that a molecule possesses. A molecule gets its properties from its structure.

Water

Water is essential as a medium for metabolic reactions; it is a constituent of cells; key elements are found in aqueous solution; it provides a habitat for aquatic organisms.

Water has 5 important properties:

- **Water is a polar** molecule. This means that it has an unequal distribution of electrical charge, with a negative charge on its hydroxyl ions and positive charge on its hydrogen ions. Water is therefore a good solvent for many substances. Ionic solids, like salt, and polar molecules, such as sugar and amino acids, readily dissolve in it. Lipids are non-polar and are therefore insoluble in water.
  Water molecules join together by attractive forces. The positively charged hydrogen atoms of one molecule are attracted to the negatively charged oxygen atoms of nearby water molecules. This hydrogen-oxygen attraction is known as **hydrogen bonding**.
- Water has a high **specific heat** i.e. a large amount of heat energy is needed to cause a small rise in temperature. This is important:
  ✓ inside cells, where metabolic reactions are enzyme controlled.
  ✓ externally to provide a constant environment for aquatic organisms.
- Water has a high **latent heat** i.e. a great deal of heat energy is needed to change it from a liquid to a vapour state, e.g. this is important in temperature control where heat is used for vapourisation of water when sweating.
- Water has a **maximum density at 4°C**. Ice floats and the warmest water is at the bottom of a lake.
- At ordinary temperatures water has the **highest surface tension** of any liquid except mercury. Surface tension allows the surface film of standing water to support aquatic insects.

Carbohydrates

Chemical compounds are divided into 2 groups, organic and inorganic. All the complex compounds of carbon are included in the organic group.
Carbohydrates are **organic compounds** containing **carbon, hydrogen and oxygen.**
Carbohydrates are of three types – **monosaccharides, disaccharides,** and **polysaccharides**.
They have two main **functions**:
- a source of energy in both plants and animals, e.g. sugars, starch, glycogen.
- a structural role in plant cell walls, e.g. cellulose.

Monosaccharides

Monosaccharides are relatively small organic molecules called **monomers.**
They have the general formula $(CH_2O)n$ where n is any number from 3 to 9.
n = 3 triose - important in metabolism.
n = 5 pentoses - used in the formation of nucleic acids.
n = 6 hexoses, e.g. glucose, the main source of energy.

❏ **Action** Draw diagrams of straight chain glucose and ring glucose.

All sugars share the formula $C_6H_{12}O_6$ but they differ in their molecular structure, they are isomers. Glucose exists as two isomers, the α form and the β form. These different forms result in considerable biological differences when they form polymers such as starch and cellulose.

Disaccharides

Disaccharides consist of two monosaccharide units linked together by the formation of a **glycosidic bond** *with the elimination of water*. This is a **condensation** reaction.

Monosaccharides			Disaccharide	Where found
glucose	+	glucose	= maltose	malt sugar
glucose	+	fructose	= sucrose	cane sugar
glucose	+	galactose	= lactose	milk sugar

❏ **Action**
1. Draw a molecule of maltose formed by the joining of two molecules of glucose.
2. Make sure you know the difference between a reducing and non-reducing sugar and the appropriate food test.

Polysaccharides

Polysaccharides are large, complex molecules called **polymers.** They are formed from very large numbers of monosaccharide units linked together. The two main groups to consider are:

- **Starch** (in plants) and **glycogen** (in animals) are **storage** polysaccharides, because glucose can be added or removed easily. These are built up of α glucose molecules.
  ✓ they are compact molecules making them ideal as energy stores.
  ✓ they are insoluble and have no osmotic effect in cells.
- **Cellulose** has a **structural** role as it gives a high tensile strength to **plant cell walls**. Cellulose consists of long chains of β glucose molecules cross-linked to each other by hydrogen bonds. Being made up of β glucose units, the chain has adjacent glucose molecules rotated by 180°. This allows hydrogen bonds to be formed between the hydroxyl groups of adjacent parallel chains, and helps to give cellulose its structural stability. These chains are grouped together into microfibrils.

❏ **Action** Draw a simplified arrangement of cellulose showing cross bridges of H bonds.

Polysaccharide	Monomer	Glycosidic bond
starch (amylose)	α glucose	1-4
glycogen	α glucose	1-4 and 1-6
cellulose	β glucose	1-4

Fats(lipids)

Like carbohydrates, lipids also contain carbon, hydrogen and oxygen but the oxygen content is very low. Lipids are formed by condensation reactions between **glycerol** and molecules of **fatty acids**.

In this reaction water is removed and an oxygen bond, known as an **ester bond**, is formed between the glycerol and fatty acid.

❏ **Action**

Draw one molecule of glycerol + 3 molecules of fatty acids forming a triglyceride + water.
(structural formula)   (general formula)

4

Glycerol is hydrophilic and fatty acids are hydrophobic.

Most naturally occurring lipids contain glycerol but they differ according to the nature of the fatty acids. The general formula of a **saturated** fatty acid is $CH_3(CH_2)n\ COOH$ (where n = an even number between 14 and 22). Some fatty acids contain one or more double bonds and therefore have fewer hydrogen atoms than they might. They are said to be **unsaturated**.

A high intake of fat, notably saturated fats, is a contributory factor in heart disease.

The chemical **properties** of lipids are:
- they are insoluble in water but dissolve in organic solvents.
- fats are solid at room temperature whereas oils are liquids.

The functions of fats include:
- **energy storage**. Fats are used as an energy store in seeds and animals, rather than carbohydrates, because one gram of fat yields approximately twice as much energy as one gram of carbohydrate.
- heat **insulator**.
- **protecting** delicate internal organs.

Phospholipids

Phospholipids are lipids in which:
- one of the fatty acid groups is replaced by a phosphate group.
- the phosphate group is hydrophilic (polar).
- the rest of the molecule is hydrophobic (non-polar).

❑ ***Action***   Draw the structure of a phospholipid.

Phospholipids are important in the formation and functioning of membranes in cells (see page 12).

Proteins

- Proteins are built up from linear sequences of **amino acids.** About 20 different amino acids are used to make up proteins. The amino acids differ by the –R group.

❑ ***Action***   Draw the structural formula of a generalised amino acid

(You are not expected to recall names of amino acids but you should be able to identify them given a structural formula and a table showing –R groups.)
- Proteins differ from carbohydrates and lipids in that in addition to carbon, hydrogen and oxygen they always contain nitrogen. Many proteins also contain sulphur and sometimes phosphorous.
- Proteins possess an **amino group**, NH_2^-, at one end of the molecule, and a **carboxyl group**, –COOH, at the other end.

Properties of proteins

Proteins are:
- crystalline and colourless.
- amphoteric and so can act as buffers.

Structure of proteins

Proteins are built up from a linear sequence of amino acids. The amino group of one amino acid reacts with the carboxyl group of another with the elimination of water. The bond that is formed is called a **peptide bond** and the resulting compound is a **dipeptide**. A number of amino acids joined in this way is called a **polypeptide**.

❑ *Action*

> Draw the structural formulae of two amino acids showing the removal of one molecule of water and the formation of a dipeptide. Label the peptide link.

Four **levels of protein structure** exist:

- The **primary structure** of a protein is the sequence of amino acid in its polypeptide chain. The proteins differ from each other in the variety, numbers and orders of their constituent amino acids linked by **peptide bonds** only.
- The **secondary structure** is the shape that the polypeptide chain forms as a result of hydrogen bonding. This is most often a spiral known as the α helix. (An alternative is a pleated sheet occurring as a flat zig-zag chain but no details of this are required).
- The **tertiary structure** is formed by the bending and twisting of the polypeptide helix into a compact structure. The shape is maintained by **disulphide, ionic** and **hydrogen bonds**. e.g. globular proteins.
- The **quaternary structure** arises from a combination of two or more polypeptide chains in tertiary form. These are associated with non-protein groups and form large, complex molecules, e.g. haemoglobin.

Classification of proteins

Proteins can be classified according to their structure:

- **Fibrous** proteins e.g. keratin and collagen, perform structural functions. They are:
- ✓ insoluble in water.
- ✓ strong and tough.
- ✓ made up of long polypeptide chains or sheets often with numerous cross linkages.
- **Globular** proteins (function as enzymes, antibodies, plasma proteins and hormones). They are:
- ✓ folded as globular or spherical molecules.
- ✓ soluble in water.

❑ *Action*

1. In a table or flowchart form make a summary of the structure, occurrence, properties and functions of proteins.
2. You should be able to use given structural formulae (proteins, triglycerides and carbohydrates) to show how bonds are formed and broken by condensation and hydrolysis, including peptide, glycosidic and ester bonds.
   You should be able to recognise and understand but not reproduce the structural formulae of these molecules.
3. Make a list of key words and write definitions of each.
4. Make sure that you can relate the structure of carbohydrates, fats and proteins to their functions.

1.2 Cell Structure

Internal cell membranes

Membranes within the cell are important as:
- They separate areas from the rest of the cytoplasm e.g. potentially harmful chemicals and/or enzymes can be isolated in an organelle so that they do not damage the rest of the cell.
- Many metabolic processes involve enzymes and membranes provide a large surface area for their attachment.
- The synthesis of ATP in respiration and photosynthesis takes place on the membranes found in mitochondria and chloroplasts respectively.
- They provide a transport system within the cell.

Cell organelles

❑ **Action**   1. Draw and label a cell as seen with an electron microscope.
             2. Draw and label the following organelles where appropriate.

Mitochondrion
The mitochondrion is bounded by two thin membranes separated by a narrow fluid-filled inter-membrane space. The inner membrane is folded inwards to form extensions called **cristae**. The interior contains an organic **matrix** containing numerous chemical compounds. The chemical reactions of aerobic respiration take place in the mitochondrion. Some of the reactions take place in the matrix, while others occur on the inner membrane and in the **cytosol**. The cristae increase the surface area on which the respiratory processes take place. The function of mitochondria is to produce energy as ATP.

Rough and smooth endoplasmic reticulum (ER)
(If you use an abbreviation in an exam you must give the full term the first time you use it).
The cytoplasm is a highly organised material consisting of a soluble ground substance called the cytosol . This contains an elaborate system of parallel, flattened sacs, **cisternae**, continuous with the nuclear membrane and may link to the golgi body. The cavities are interconnected and this system is known as the **endoplasmic reticulum** (ER). There are two types of ER:
- **rough ER** – which have the membranes lined with ribosomes. The rough ER functions in protein synthesis as a transport system.
- **smooth ER** – which have membranes lacking ribosomes. These are concerned with the synthesis and transport of lipids.

Ribosomes
These are made up of one large and one small sub-unit and are made up of ribosomal RNA and protein. They are important in **protein synthesis** where they move along m RNA in succession.

Golgi body/ apparatus

This is similar in structure to ER but is more compact. It is made up of a series of dynamic, flattened sacs which function in packaging proteins for secretion by the coalescence of vesicles at one end and budding off at the other. Its functions include:

- Producing secretory enzymes.
- Secreting carbohydrates.
- Producing glycoprotein.
- Transporting and storing lipids.
- Forming lysosomes.

Lysosome

The lysosome contains and isolates digestive enzymes from the remainder of the cell. Digestion is carried out in a membrane-lined vacuole into which several lysosomes may discharge their contents. One of their functions is to destroy worn out organelles in the cell.

Centrioles

Centrioles are found in all animal cells and most protoctists but are absent from the cells of higher plants. Centrioles arise in a distinct region of the cytoplasm known as the **centrosome** and consist of two hollow cylinders. At **cell division** they migrate to opposite poles of the cell where they synthesise the microtubules of the spindle

Chloroplast

The chloroplast is found in plant cells only. It is bounded by a **double outer membrane.** Within the chloroplast are two regions:

the **stroma**, which is a colourless, gelatinous matrix containing ribosomes, lipid, circular DNA and possibly starch. In the stroma are embedded the grana.

the **grana,** each being made up of between 2 and 100 closed, parallel, flattened sacs called **thylakoids**, within which are found the photosynthetic pigments such as chlorophyll. Some thylakoids have tubular extensions which interconnect adjacent grana

Vacuole

A vacuole is a fluid-filled sac bounded by a single membrane.

In animal cells vacuoles:

- are small vesicles and may occur in large numbers.
- may be formed during phagocytosis or act as contractile vacuoles.

In plant cells :

- there is usually one large central vacuole and the single membrane around it is called a tonoplast.
- vacuoles function as storage sites and provide an osmotic system which functions in support of young tissues.

Nucleus

This is the most prominent feature in the cell. Its function is to control the cell's activities and to retain the chromosomes. The nucleus is bounded by a double membrane, the **nuclear envelope**. This has pores in it to allow the transport of m RNA and nucleotides. The cytoplasm-like material within the nucleus is called the **nucleoplasm**. It contains **chromatin**, which is made up of coils of DNA bound to protein. During cell division the chromatin condenses to form the chromosomes. Within the nucleus are one or two small spherical bodies, each called a **nucleolus**. These are thought to manufacture ribosomal RNA. and assemble ribosomes.

Additional structures

♦ **Cellulose cell wall**

This is only found in plant cells. It consists of cellulose microfibrils embedded in a polysaccharide matrix. The main functions of a cell wall are:
✓ to provide strength and support.
✓ to permit the movement of water from cell to cell.

♦ **Plasmodesmata**

The cell wall is interrupted at intervals by narrow pores carrying fine strands of cytoplasm which join the living cells to one another. The plasmodesmata contain endoplasmic reticulum which is therefore continuous from cell to cell and facilitate the movement of materials between cells.

1.2 Cell organisation

Prokaryote and eukaryote cells

Prokaryote cells were probably the first life forms on Earth. This type of cell is found in bacteria and blue-green algae. **Eukaryote** cells are typical of the great majority of organisms including all animals and plants.

Prokaryotic cells	Eukaryotic cells
• no membrane bound organelles	membrane bound organelles
• DNA is circular and lies free in the cytoplasm	DNA in linear chromosomes, combined with histone proteins
• no nuclear membrane or ER	distinct membrane-bound nucleus
• ribosomes are smaller	ribosomes are larger

In prokaryotes the cell wall is not made of cellulose; the site of respiration is infoldings of the cell membrane, mesosomes; a protective layer or capsule may be present; small circular structures of DNA, plasmids, may be present.

❏ *Action*   Draw a labelled diagram of a bacterium.

Viruses

Viruses are extremely small and cannot be seen using the light microscope. They enter living cells and multiply with the assistance of the host cells. Viruses cause a variety of infectious diseases in humans, other animals and plants.

Each virus particle, or virion, is made up of a core of **nucleic acid** surrounded by a **protein coat**, the capsid. Most viruses are found in animal cells and those attacking bacteria (bacteriophages) have the nucleic acid DNA.

❏ *Action*   Draw and label a typical virus.

Differences between plant and animal cells

❏ *Action*   Draw and label a typical plant and typical animal cell as seen using a light microscope.

Structure	Plant cell	Animal cell
plasma/cell surface membrane	present	present
membrane bound nucleus	present	present
nucleolus	present	present
chromatin	present	present
mitochondria	present	present
rough and smooth ER	present	present
ribosomes	present	present
golgi body/apparatus	present	present
chloroplasts	present	absent
cell wall and plasmodesmata	present	absent
large vacuole and tonoplast	present	absent
centriole	absent	present

❏ *Action*   Construct a table to compare the structure of animal, plant and prokaryote cells and viruses.

Levels of organisation

❑ *Action*

> Look up these terms **- Acellular, multicellular, cell, tissue, organ, organ system.**

Differentiation is the process by which unspecialised structures become modified and specialised for the performance of specific functions.
Division of labour - when cells become specialised for one function they often lose the ability to carry out other functions.

❑ *Action*

> Examine, using the microscope, the histology of cuboidal and ciliated **epithelium,** smooth and striated **muscle,** collagen **connective** tissue.

1.3 Cell membrane

The cell surface membrane or plasma membrane is the boundary that separates the living cell from its nonliving surroundings.

Structure of the membrane
It made up almost entirely of **proteins** and **phospholipids**.
The Fluid Mosaic model was suggested by Singer and Nicholson. They proposed that:
- there is a **bimolecular phospholipid** layer with inwardly hydrophobic(non polar) lipid tails and outwardly directed hydrophilic(polar) phosphate heads.
- Associated with the bilayer is a variety of protein molecules:
- ✓ some of the proteins occur on or in only one of the layers(extrinsic proteins).
- ✓ some proteins extend across both layers (intrinsic proteins).
- the phospholipid layer is capable of movement i.e. it is fluid and in surface view the proteins are dotted throughout the layer in a mosaic arrangement.
- The model is referred to as the 'fluid mosaic' model because the components are free to move with respect to each other.

❑ *Action*   Draw a diagram showing the fluid mosaic structure of the cell membrane.

The main functions of the cell membrane include:
- structural support
- secreting chemicals
- cell–cell recognition and surface recognition by enzymes, hormones and antibodies
- taking up nutrients and other requirements.

The membrane as a barrier
The cell surface membrane is selectively permeable to water and some solutes. Lipid-soluble substances can move through the cell membrane more easily than water-soluble substances.
- The hydrophobic core of the membrane impedes the transport of ions and polar molecules.
  These require specific transport proteins.
- Very small molecules that are polar but uncharged e.g. water, can pass through the membrane.
- small, uncharged molecules, such as oxygen and carbon dioxide, freely cross as they are soluble in the lipid part of the membrane.
- charged particles(ions), and relatively large molecules such as glucose, do not readily pass through the membrane because they are relatively insoluble in lipid. Certain proteins assist such particles to pass in or out of the cell. These proteins are of two types:
- ✓ channel proteins
- ✓ carrier proteins.

1.3 Transport across cell membranes

Diffusion

Diffusion is the **movement of molecules or ions** from a region where they are in high concentration to a region of lower concentration. Ions and molecules are always in a state of **random movement** but if they are highly concentrated in one area there will be a net movement away from that area until equilibrium is reached or until there is a uniform distribution. The rate of diffusion depends on:
- the concentration gradient – the steeper the gradient the faster the rate.
- the distance over which it takes place- the shorter the distance the greater the rate.
- the surface area – the larger the surface area the greater the rate.
- temperature – an increase in temperature results in an increase in rate since there is an increase in molecular energy and therefore movement.

Facilitated diffusion

Charged particles or ions and large molecules such as glucose, do not readily pass through the cell membrane because they are relatively insoluble in lipid. In the cell membrane protein molecules span the membrane from one side to the other and help such particles to diffuse in or out of the cells. These proteins are of two types:
- **channel proteins** – these channels form water- filled pores in the membrane. As the channel is hydrophilic, water soluble substances can pass through. The channels are selective and in this way the cell can control the entry and exit of molecules and ions.
- **carrier proteins** – these bind molecules to them and then change shape as a result of this binding in such a way that the molecules are released on the other side of the membrane. They conduct molecules in either direction and energy from ATP is not needed.

❑ *Action*

    Draw a diagram to show facilitated diffusion by carrier proteins.

Osmosis

Most cell membranes are permeable to water and certain solutes only. In biological systems osmosis is a special form of diffusion which involves the movement of **water molecules only.**

Osmosis is the movement of water from a region where it is highly concentrated to a region where it is lower, through a partially permeable membrane.

The term **water potential (WP)** ψ(psi) is used by biologists to describe the tendency of water molecules to move from high to low concentrations, i.e. water will move from a region of high WP to one of lower WP. This is because where there is a high concentration of water molecules they have a greater potential energy. A higher WP implies a greater tendency to leave. The WP of pure water is zero, so all solutions have lower WPs than pure water and are given negative values. Water will diffuse from a region of less negative (higher) WP to one of more negative (lower) WP.

In plant cells:

$$\psi \qquad = \qquad \psi_s \qquad + \qquad \psi_p$$

water potential   solute potential   pressure potential

- **Water potential** is the capacity of a system to lose water.
- The presence of solute molecules in the vacuole of a plant cell lowers the WP. This change in WP due to the presence of solute molecules is called the **solute potential**.
- When water enters a plant cell vacuole by osmosis a hydrostatic pressure is set up and pushes outwards on the cell wall. This is known as the **pressure potential**.

Turgor and plasmolysis
(The terms hypertonic, hypotonic and isotonic should really only be applied to animal cells. If the WP of the external solution is lower than the solution inside the cell it is **hypertonic** and water flows out of the cell. If the WP of the external solution is higher than the solution inside the cell it is **hypotonic** and water flows into the cell. If the cell has the same solute concentration as the surrounding solution the external solution is **isotonic** with the cell.)

Turgor is important in plants. It supports them and maintains their shape and form.
- When a plant cell loses water it shrinks. The cytoplasm of a plant cell will draw away from the cell wall. This condition is called **plasmolysis** and the cell is said to be **flaccid.**
- A plant cell will gain water if placed in a hypotonic solution and will continue to take in water until prevented by the opposing wall pressure. When the cell can not take in any more water it is **turgid**.
- An animal cell will burst if placed in a hypotonic solution as it has no cell wall.

❑ *Action*
1. Draw labelled diagrams of a flaccid and a turgid plant cell.
2. Make a list of key terms and their definitions.
3. Be prepared to use the given equation in calculations.

Phagocytosis and pinocytosis
- Both phagocytosis and pinocytosis are methods by which materials are taken into the cell in bulk.
- This process is called **endocytosis**.
- **Phagocytosis** is the process by which the cell can obtain **particles** that are too large to be taken in by diffusion or active transport. A large particle may enter the cell and become enclosed by a membrane to form a vesicle and is transported through the cytoplasm.
- Secretion or exocytosis refers to substances leaving the cell after being transported through the cytoplasm in a vesicle.
- Through phagocytosis and secretion, the cell membrane is continually having portions removed or added to it.
- **Pinocytosis** is entry of **liquid** by the same mechanism of phagocytosis, except that the vesicles produced are smaller.

❑ *Action*
Draw a diagram to illustrate phagocytosis.

Active transport
Unlike the processes described so far, active transport is an **energy requiring** process in which **ions** and **molecules** are **moved** across membranes **against a concentration gradient**.

The features of active transport are:
- Ions and molecules can move in the opposite direction to that in which diffusion occurs, i.e. against a concentration gradient.
- The energy is supplied by ATP, and anything which affects the respiratory process will affect active transport.
- The process will not take place in the presence of a respiratory inhibitor such as cyanide.
- The process occurs through the carrier proteins that span the membrane. The proteins accept the molecule and then the molecule enters the cell by a change in shape of the carrier molecule.

❏ *Action*

Draw diagrams to show how the carrier proteins change shape when conveying a molecule across the membrane.

1.4   Enzymes

Metabolic reactions occur quickly and thousands of reactions are taking place at the same time in cells. Order and control is essential if reactions are not to interfere with each other. These features of metabolism are made possible by the action of enzymes.

Properties of enzymes

Enzymes:
- are large **protein** (globular) molecules.
- act as **catalysts.**
- lower **activation energy**.
- are **reversible** in their action.
- are very efficient, having high **turnover numbers**.
- can be **denatured** by heat.
- Most enzymes are **specific**.

❑ *Action*   Explain the above statements in detail.

How enzymes work

Enzymes react with another molecule called a **substrate.** Each enzyme has its own special shape, with an area, the **active site**, onto which the substrate molecules bind.
Modern interpretations of the lock and key theory suggest that in the presence of the substrate the active site may change in order to select the substrate's shape. This is called the **induced fit hypothesis**. This may be illustrated by the enzyme, lysozyme, but structural details are not required.

enzyme + substrate = enzyme–substrate complex = enzyme + product.

❑ *Action*   Draw a diagram to illustrate the above equation.

Factors affecting enzyme action

Enzymes are made inside living cells but may act inside the cell (intracellular) or outside (intercellular, extracellular) such as the digestive enzymes of the alimentary canal.
Environmental conditions such as temperature and pH change the three dimensional structure of enzyme molecules. Bonds are broken and hence the configuration of the active site is altered.
Various factors influence the action of enzymes.
- **Temperature** – the rate of an enzyme catalysed reaction increases with increasing temperature due to increased frequency of collisions.
- ✓ enzymes are denatured by temperatures above 45°C.
- ✓ their optimum temperature is about 37°C.
- ✓ at low temperatures e.g. freezing, enzymes are inactive.
- **pH** – the rate of an enzyme catalysed reaction will vary with changes in pH.
- ✓ enzymes have a narrow optimum range.
- ✓ deviations from this optimum may result in denaturation.
- ✓ small changes in pH cause small reversible changes in enzyme structure and results in inactivation.
- **substrate concentration** – the rate of an enzyme catalysed reaction will vary with changes in substrate concentration.

The *Michaelis constant* is the concentration of substrate needed to make the reaction proceed at half its maximum rate. A low Michaelis constant means the reaction proceeds rapidly because the enzyme and substrate have a high affinity for each other.

- **enzyme concentration** – the rate of an enzyme catalysed reaction will vary with changes in enzyme concentration.

Enzymes and digestion

- The functions of the following enzymes in the human alimentary canal:
- ✓ salivary amylase.
- ✓ rennin; pepsin activated from pepsinogen, acid.
- ✓ sodium hydrogen carbonate neutralises acid, lipase, trypsin activated from trypsinogen, enterokinase.
- The physiological significance of the effects of temperature, pH, activation and inactivation on digestive enzymes.

❑ ***Action***

1. Make a list of key terms and give a definition for each term.
2. Draw separate graphs to illustrate the effect of the above factors on enzyme action.
3. Describe, **in detail**, the shape of the graph in each case.
4. Make notes on the enzymes involved in digestion with specific reference to the conditions required for optimum enzyme action.

Enzyme experiments

You are expected to carry out investigations that show progression from GCSE to AS. Examples of enzyme experiments might include:
- ✓ the effect of rennet and hydrochloric acid on enzymes during digestion.
- ✓ the effect of pH on the rate of conversion of starch to maltose by amylase etc.

In enzyme experiments it is essential that buffers and controls are used.
- ✓ **Buffers** maintain a constant pH – in a buffer solution the pH changes little when a small quantity of acid or alkali is added.
- ✓ **Control** – controls are duplicate experiments, identical in every respect to the actual experiment, except for the variable being investigated, which is kept constant.

Enzymes and inhibitors

- The rate of enzyme controlled reactions may be decreased by the presence of inhibitors.
- Inhibition occurs when enzyme action is slowed down or stopped by another substance.

Reversible inhibition

The effect of this type of inhibitor is **temporary**. There is no permanent damage to the enzyme because the association of the inhibitor with the enzyme is a loose one. Removal of the inhibitor allows the enzyme to function normally. There are two types of reversible inhibitors:

- **Competitive**, where the inhibitor is **structurally similar to the substrate** and associates with the enzyme active site. E.g. Malonic acid competes with succinate for the active sites of succinic dehydrogenase, an important enzyme in the Krebs cycle in respiration. If the substrate concentration is increased so will the rate of reaction. The more substrate molecules the greater the chance of finding active sites, leaving fewer to be occupied by the inhibitor.

- **Non-competitive**, where the inhibitor has **no resemblance to the substrate** molecule and binds to the enzyme at a site away from the active site. This alters the shape of the enzyme molecule in such a way that the active site can no longer accommodate the substrate. As the substrate and inhibitor molecules attach to different parts of the enzyme they are not competing for the same sites. The rate of reaction is therefore unaffected by substrate concentration.
E.g. Cyanide attaches itself to part of the enzyme, cytochrome oxidase and inhibits respiration.

Non-reversible inhibition
These leave the enzyme permanently damaged e.g. mercury breaks the disulphide bonds which maintain the shape of the enzyme molecule.
(You are not required to use the terms 'reversible' and 'non-reversible' in an exam. They have been included as you may come across the terms in a text book.)

End product inhibition
In some metabolic pathways the end product of the pathway may act as an inhibitor. This end product inhibition is an example of a negative feedback mechanism preventing the unnecessary accumulation of a metabolite.

❑ *Action*
> Draw diagrams to illustrate the different types of inhibition.

1.5 Applications of enzymes

Enzymes are used on a wide commercial scale in the food, pharmaceutical and agrochemical industries. You are required to learn about two particular applications:

- **Immobilised enzymes**
Immobilised enzymes are used widely in industrial processes, such as fermentation, as they can readily be recovered for reuse.
There are four main methods of immobilising enzymes. Each method has its own advantages and disadvantages and no one method is ideal for all situations.
✓ entrapment
✓ adsorption
✓ cross-linking
✓ covalent bonding
(You are not required to know the details of these methods but to appreciate that the immobilisation of enzymes involves enmeshing the enzyme in a matrix or inert solid support to improve stability and ease of reuse.)

Advantages of immobilised enzymes
Enzyme instability is one of the key factors that prevent their wider use. Chemicals such as organic solvents, raised temperatures and pH values outside the norm can denature the enzyme with a consequent loss of activity. Immobilising enzymes with a polymer matrix creates a microenvironment.
By allowing processes to occur at higher temperatures than normal means that activity is increased and so production is increased.
In addition to **stabilising** the enzyme against heat or solvent effects other advantages include:

✓ Enzymes can **tolerate** a wider range of conditions.
✓ Enzymes are **easily recovered** for re-use thus reducing overall costs.
✓ **Several enzymes** with differing pH or temperature optima **can be used together**.
✓ Enzymes can be **easily added or removed** giving greater control over the reaction.

- **Biosensors**

Biosensors work on the principle that enzymes are **specific** and they select one type of molecule from a mixture even in very **low concentrations**. They can be used for the **rapid** and **accurate** detection of minute traces of biologically important molecules.

The term 'biosensor' describes the association of a biomolecule, such as an enzyme, with a transducer which produces an electrical signal in response to substrate transformation. The strength of the electrical signal may be measured with a suitable meter.
Their uses include:
✓ pregnancy testing kits.
✓ monitoring blood sugar levels in diabetics.
✓ in fermenters to provide a rapid, sensitive and specific measurement of products.

Diabetes – the glucose oxidase testing of urine
The quick and accurate measurement of glucose is of great importance medically, e.g. testing urine for the presence and concentration of glucose.
The chemical changes occur as follows:
Glucose oxidase catalyses the following reaction.
$$\beta \text{ D-glucose} + \text{oxygen} = \text{gluconic acid} + H_2O_2$$

A simple quantitative procedure can be devised by coupling the production of hydrogen peroxide to the activity of the enzyme peroxidase which catalyses the oxidation of a colourless hydrogen donor to produce a coloured product. The amount of compound D produced is a direct measure of the amount of glucose that reacts.
$$DH_2 \quad + \quad H_2O_2 \quad = \quad 2H_2O \quad + \quad D$$
colourless   coloured

Glucose oxidase is immobilised onto the surface of an electrode by being enclosed in small alginate beads. The electrode can detect changes in substrate or product, temperature changes or optical properties. When the glucose oxidase–oxygen electrode probe is placed into a solution suspected to contain glucose, the glucose diffuses into the immobilised enzyme layer and immediately oxygen is taken up.

❑ *Action*
       1. Draw and label a biosensor.
       2. Construct a table of comparison between 'free' and immobilised enzymes.

Steps in the functioning of a biosensor
1. Blood contains a mixture of different molecules.
2. Enzyme electrode is placed in a blood sample.
3. Glucose diffuses into the immobilised enzyme layer.
4. Oxygen is taken up.
5. The rate of oxygen uptake is proportional to the glucose concentration.
6. A digital display shows an accurate concentration of glucose.

1.6   Nucleic acids

Nucleic acids

Nucleic acids are built up of units called **nucleotides**.
Individual nucleotides are made up of **three parts** that combine by condensation reactions.
These are:
- **phosphoric acid** (phosphate H_3PO_4). This has the same structure in all nucleotides.
- **pentose sugar**, of which there are two types:
  ✓ in ribonucleic acid (RNA) the sugar is ribose.
  ✓ in deoxyribonucleic acid (DNA) the sugar is deoxyribose.
- **organic base**.

There are five different bases which are divided into two groups:
- the **pyrimidine** bases are thymine, cytosine and uracil.
- the **purine** bases are adenine and guanine.

Deoxyribonucleic acid (DNA)

The structure of DNA
- It is a double stranded polymer of nucleotides or **polynucleotide**. (A polymer is a large number of repeating units.)
- Each polynucleotide may contain many million nucleotide units.
- It is in the form of a **double helix**, the shape of which is maintained by hydrogen bonding.
- The pentose sugar is always **deoxyribose**.
- DNA contains four **organic bases**. These are adenine, guanine, cytosine, and thymine.
- Each strand is linked to the other by pairs of organic bases.
- Cytosine always pairs with guanine, adenine always pairs with thymine, and the bases are joined by hydrogen bonds.

❑ *Action*   Draw a part of a DNA chain showing a polynucleotide consisting of three base pairs.

DNA performs two major functions:
1. **Replication** in dividing cells.
2. Carrying the information for **protein synthesis**.

Ribonucleic acid (RNA)

The structure of RNA
- RNA is a **single stranded** polymer of nucleotide.
- RNA contains the pentose sugar, **ribose**.
- RNA contains the organic **bases** adenine, guanine, cytosine, and uracil.

There are three types of RNA:
- **ribosomal RNA (rRNA)** is found in the cytoplasm and is a large, complex molecule made up of both double and single helices.
- **transfer RNA (tRNA)** is a small single stranded molecule. It forms a clover-leaf shape, with one end of the chain ending in a cytosine-cytosine-adenine sequence at which point

the amino acid it carries attaches itself. At the opposite end of the chain is a sequence of three bases called the **anticodon**.

- **messenger RNA (mRNA)** is a long single-stranded molecule, formed into a helix. It is manufactured in the nucleus and passes into the cytoplasm where it associates with the ribosomes.

❑ *Action*
1. Make drawings of the different types of RNA.
2. Construct a table of differences between DNA and RNA.

1.6 Replication and protein synthesis

DNA has two major functions in the cell:
- **Replication**, in dividing cells.
- Carrying information for **protein synthesis** in all cells.

Replication

When cells divide, each daughter cell must receive an exact copy of the genetic material. It is the DNA molecule which replicates or makes copies of itself. It does this as follows:
- **DNA unwinds** and as the strands separate **DNA polymerase** catalyses the addition of free nucleotides to the exposed bases.
- Each chain acts as a **template** so that free nucleotides can be joined to their **complementary bases** by DNA polymerase.
- The final result is two DNA molecules each made up of one newly synthesised chain and one chain that has been conserved from the original molecule.
- This is called the **semi-conservative hypothesis** and was proposed by Meselsohn and Stahl.
1. They cultured the bacterium, *Escherichia coli*, for several generations on a medium containing the **heavy** isotope of nitrogen, N_{15}.
2. The bacteria were transferred to a medium containing the lighter, more common form of nitrogen, N_{14}.
3. They could distinguish DNA of different densities by centrifuging DNA extracted from the bacteria.
   (A centrifuge can spin tubes containing liquid suspensions at a very high speed. The denser particles will separate out at a lower point in the tube than the lighter particles.)
   (a) Any new DNA that the bacteria made would be lighter than the "old" DNA made in the N_{15} medium.
   (b) The bacteria incorporated the N_{15} into their nucleotides and then into their DNA.

- ❏ *Action*
   1. Using coloured pens draw a diagram to show how two complementary strands of DNA unwind into separate strands. Starting with the parent strands carry out the process for three generations.
   2. Make sure that you can interpret the evidence of Meselsohn and Stahl's experiments.

Nature of the genetic code

DNA is the starting point for protein synthesis since the sequence of bases on DNA (genetic code) determines the primary structure of a protein, i.e. the sequence by which various amino acids are joined together to form a particular polypeptide chain.
The codes carried by DNA determine what reactions can take place in an organism. Genes control the formation of enzymes which are proteins and by determining which enzymes are produced the DNA can determine the organism's characteristics.
- It is the sequence of bases in the DNA chain that codes for the sequence of amino acids in a polypeptide.
- the portion of DNA which codes for a whole polypeptide is called a **gene**. (This is the basis of the one gene–one polypeptide hypothesis.)

- Each amino acid is coded for by three bases (the triplet code),called a **codon**. Since there are four bases, the number of different codons that are possible is sixty four, more than enough to code for twenty different amino acids.
- all the codons are **universal** i.e. they are exactly the same for all organisms.
- the code is **non-overlapping**, in that each triplet is read separately.

Protein synthesis

There are four main stages in the formation of a protein:
1. the **synthesis** of amino acids;
2. **transcription** (formation of messenger RNA);
3. amino acid **activation**;
4. **translation**.

DNA in the nucleus acts as a template for the production of mRNA, which conveys the instructions needed for protein synthesis from the nucleus to the cytoplasm. The function of the ribosomes is to provide a suitable surface for the attachment of mRNA and the assembly of protein.

The process of protein synthesis occurs as follows:
- **RNA polymerase** links to the DNA at the beginning of the sequence to be transcribed. A very short section of the DNA molecule carries the code for the synthesis of a polypeptide chain. The double-stranded DNA first untwists and then unzips in the relevant region. Only one of the DNA strands acts as a template.
- Transcription occurs when free RNA nucleotides then align themselves opposite one of the two strands. Because of the complementary relationship between the bases in DNA and the free nucleotides, cytosine in the DNA attracts a guanine, guanine a cytosine, thymine an adenine, and adenine a uracil.
- **RNA polymerase** moves along the DNA picking up appropriate free RNA nucleotides from the nucleoplasm. This results in the synthesis of a molecule of mRNA alongside the unzipped portion of DNA.. This process is called **transcription.** The mRNA moves through the nuclear pore and attaches itself to a ribosome.
- At the end of the sequence the m RNA is detached and the DNA rewinds.
- m RNA transfers nucleotides through the nuclear pores to the cytoplasm where it attaches to ribosomes consisting of ribosomal RNA and protein.
- mRNA is held by a ribosome which has two transfer RNA (tRNA) binding sites. One site binds tRNA with the growing polypeptide the other site is for tRNA and the next amino acid in the sequence i.e. the tRNA molecule has an anticodon and a specific amino acid binding site.
- **Activation** is the process by which amino acids combine with **transfer RNA** (tRNA) using energy from ATP. Each type of tRNA binds with a specific amino acid. The tRNA molecules with attached amino acids now move towards the ribosome.
- **translation** by ribosomes allows assembly of amino acids into polypeptides according to the original DNA code. A ribosomal enzyme catalyses peptide bond formation between an amino acid on one tRNA and the growing polypeptide on the other tRNA.
- A ribosome passes along mRNA, one codon at a time, tRNA with the appropriate anticodon fills the vacant slot and the amino acid forms a peptide bond with the last member of the chain using energy from ATP, until a stop codon is reached.

- The ribosome acts as a framework moving along the mRNA, reading the code, holding the **codon-anticodon complex** together until two amino acids join. The ribosome moves along adding one amino acid at a time until the polypeptide chain is assembled.
- A group of ribosomes moving along one after the other is called a **polysome system**. Each time one ribosome moves along the mRNA a molecule of protein is produced.
- Polypeptides may be further modified and a protein may consist of more than one polypeptide.

Action

1. Draw simple diagrams to illustrate each stage in the process of protein synthesis.
2. Construct a flow diagram showing the sequence of events in protein synthesis.
3. Construct a table to show the functions of DNA, messenger RNA and transfer RNA.
4. Revise the primary, secondary, tertiary and quaternary structure of proteins.

1.6   Genetic counselling

The Human genome project

- The Human genome project has been in operation since 1996 whereby sequencing of DNA is carried out and information regarding the genes found is available on the Internet.
  Access http://www.ncbi.nlm.nih.gov/SCIENCE96/
- The aim is to provide details of all gene sequences on the human chromosomes. This will enable faulty genes to be identified and possibly rectified. However this has ethical implications:
- ✓ misuse, such as eugenics, and interfering with specific genetic characteristics which may be regarded as undesirable.
- ✓ The mapping of a gene may not lead to a cure for a condition and false hopes may be raised once genes are identified.
- ✓ Genetic analysis may be overemphasised as a predictor of health.

Genetic counselling

If a family has a history of a genetic defect unaffected members can consult a **genetic counsellor** for advice on the risk of bearing an affected child. Advice may be based on:
- History of the disorder in the family.
- Whether the parents are closely related.
- Frequency of the faulty gene in the general population.

Genetic screening
Once established that there is a risk of passing on a defective gene, there are means of investigating whether a child is affected before it is born:
- Blood tests e.g. with cystic fibrosis.
- Amniocentesis – withdrawing some of the amniotic fluid during the early stages of pregnancy. The fluid contains cells that have floated away from the surface of the embryo.
- Chorionic villus sampling – early in pregnancy (within 8-10 weeks) tiny samples of fetal tissue are withdrawn from the uterus and cells are cultured and examined under the microscope.
  On the basis of these tests the parents can decide whether or not to have the pregnancy terminated.

Gene therapy

The aim of gene therapy is to treat a genetic disease by replacing defective genes in the patient's body with copies of a new DNA sequence. There are two possible ways of doing this:
- **Germ-line therapy**, whereby the gene is replaced in the egg.
- **Somatic cell therapy** which targets cells in the affected tissues.

There are problems involved:
- ✓ Risks -new DNA sequences may activate oncogenes(cancer causing genes).
- ✓ Difficulties involved in carrying out the process- it is difficult to introduce a new genetic sequence into target cells.

How can genes be added into the genome of a mammalian cell?

1. By direct uptake into mammalian cells.
    - The DNA of a gene to be introduced is extracted from donor cells and replicated many times using the polymerase chain reaction (PCR). The purified DNA is made available to cells under conditions that induce its uptake. However, this is relatively inefficient as the rate of uptake is low.
    - Injecting the gene directly into the nucleus.
2. By replacement of treated cells.

Cystic fibrosis

Cystic fibrosis is due to an autosomal recessive allele. One person in 2000 in Britain suffers from the condition. The product of the normal gene is a component of the mucus secreted by the epithelia. Cystic fibrosis patients produce thick, sticky secretions that are unable to flow. These secretions:

1. block the pancreatic duct and prevent pancreatic enzymes from reaching the duodenum and so food digestion is incomplete.
2. clog up of the lungs leading to recurrent infections.
3. and the protective lining of the intestine is defective.

Symptoms are:
✓ Distress with breathing – frequent daily massage is needed to keep the airways open.
✓ impaired digestion.
✓ Limited absorption.
Cystic children have large appetites to try to compensate.

Microbiologists have succeeded in isolating and cloning the gene which codes for a protein needed for normal functioning. Carriers can be identified using a simple blood test.
It is hoped that an aerosol inhaler could be used to restore the missing gene to the lung cells. Liposomes may be used to introduce DNA containing the normal gene This involves wrapping the gene in lipid molecules that can pass through the membranes of lung epithelial cells. This would leave patients with their digestive problems but would solve the problem of congested and infected lungs.

❑ *Action*

1. List the advantages and disadvantages of genetic screening.
2. Consider the ethics of gene therapy. Adding genes to germ cells would mean that the genome of future individuals would be changed.

1.6   Genetic engineering

Uses of genetic engineering

- To transfer genes into bacteria, so that they can make useful products, e.g. insulin.
- To transfer genes into plants and animals, so that they acquire new characteristics, e.g. resistance to disease.
- To transfer genes into humans, so that they no longer suffer from genetic diseases, e.g. cystic fibrosis.

Recombinant DNA technology

Genetic engineering involves the introduction of engineered DNA into cells in such a way that it will replicate and be passed on to progeny cells. One important application is the introduction of DNA from various organisms into bacterial cells, which then produce a required product. Recombinant DNA is formed when a piece of 'foreign' DNA is incorporated into the circular DNA (plasmid) from a bacterium.

There are four stages in gene manipulation:
- The formation of DNA fragments including the gene wanted for replication.
- The splicing (insertion) of the DNA fragments into the vector.
- The introduction of the vector into the bacterium.
- The selection of the newly transformed organism for cultivation.

Key terms
- ➤ **Recombinant DNA** – DNA which results from the combination of fragments from two different organisms.
- ➤ **Plasmids** – circular loops of DNA found in bacteria. The plasmid is known as a **vector.**
- ➤ **Restriction enzymes** – enzymes which cut DNA molecules between specific base sequences.
- ➤ **DNA ligases** – enzymes which join together portions of DNA.
- ➤ **Reverse transcriptases** – enzymes used to synthesize DNA from m RNA in specific cells.
- ➤ **Clone** – a population of genetically identical cells or organisms.
- ➤ **Sticky ends** – the two ends of the 'foreign' DNA segment. They have a short row of unpaired bases that match the complementary bases at the two ends of the opened-up plasmid.

Target gene is removed from a donor DNA molecule
Restriction endonucleases are used to cut DNA between specific base sequences which the enzyme recognises. Most restriction enzymes split the two strands in a staggered sequence. The unpaired bases at the cut form **sticky ends**.

Donor DNA fragments are spliced into recipient DNA molecules.
Splicing involves breaking open the DNA ring of a bacterial plasmid and inserting a short piece of DNA, containing the gene for the desired product from a donor species, into it. The manufactured plasmid, pBR322, is most used, as in the transformation of *E.coli.* This plasmid carries genes for resistance to certain antibiotics and so can be selected by the use of these antibiotics in the growth media. It is a small plasmid and has unique cleavage sites for several restriction enzymes. The plasmid and the required DNA are treated with the

same restriction enzyme, e.g. Hind III, giving an open plasmid and DNA fragments with complementary sticky ends that are joined by mixing and adding the enzyme **DNA ligase**.

Recombinant DNA is copied by cloning

Once a bacterium has taken up a piece of foreign DNA successfully, the foreign DNA replicates along with the rest of the plasmid every time the bacterial cell divides. **Cloning** of the recombinant containing bacteria results in multiple copies of the recombinant genes i.e. the bacterium may divide repeatedly and give rise to a large population of bacterial cells all of which contain replicas of the foreign DNA.

Cloning of bacteria containing recombinant DNA can be carried out on an industrial scale using **fermenters**. This produces large quantities of product quickly and relatively cheaply.

Doing it in reverse

The problem of the recombinant DNA containing a lot of 'extra' material can be overcome if the modification of the DNA had already occurred. This is appropriate where the protein for which a particular portion of DNA codes is found in a particular organ. The functional mRNA will be present in large quantities in the cytoplasm.
- This mRNA can be extracted.
- The addition of **reverse transcriptase** results in the formation of a single strand of DNA (copy DNA or cDNA) containing the required gene.
- The addition of **DNA polymerase** converts this to a double strand for incorporation onto a plasmid.

❏ *Action*

1. Outline the main stages of genetic engineering using the mRNA and reverse transcriptase method.
2. Create a flowchart for the main stages in the genetic engineering of bacteria for the production of insulin.
3. Make a list of additional key terms and their definitions.

Applications of genetic engineering

Two main application areas may be considered:
- **Health care**.
- ✓ The production of human hormones e.g. insulin and growth hormones.
- ✓ The production of antibiotics and vaccines.
- ✓ Gene therapy, where cells containing non-mutant genes are substituted for the abnormal mutant cells.
- **Agriculture.**
- ✓ Genetically engineered growth hormones are used to increase meat yield.
- ✓ The development of crop plants resistant to herbicides and pests, e.g. by transferring genes that produce toxins with insecticidal properties from bacteria to higher plants such as potatoes.

The advantages and disadvantages of genetic engineering

♦ **Advantages**:
✓ Large scale production of complex proteins or peptides that cannot be made by other methods.
✓ Removes the need to use organs from mammals.
✓ Higher yielding crops, superior keeping qualities, pesticide resistance.
✓

♦ **Disadvantages:**
economics
✓ technically complicated and therefore very expensive on industrial scale.
✓ difficulty of identifying the genes of value in a huge genome.
✓ synthesis of required protein may involve several genes.
✓ treatment of human DNA with restriction enzyme produces millions of fragments which are of no use.
✓ not all eukaryote genes will express themselves in prokaryote cells.

hazards – It is impossible to predict what the consequences might be of releasing genetically engineered organisms into the environment. The potential hazards are:
✓ a new gene, on insertion, may disrupt normal gene function, e.g. a potentially dangerous microorganism with a new gene may become a dangerous pathogen if it is released into the environment.
✓ bacteria readily exchange genetic material e.g. the recombinant DNA might get into other organisms e.g. herbicide resistance might be transferred to a weed species.
✓ deliberate use of antibiotic resistant genes in *E. coli* which lives in the human gut and these genes could be accidentally transferred to human pathogens.
✓ possibility of transfer of DNA with linked pathogenic genes, e.g. oncogenes increasing cancer risks.
✓ food crops issues: dispersal of pollen containing gene, unknown effects of eating new protein produced in crop, increased use of pesticides and pesticide residues.

Genetic fingerprinting

The following background information is not required for examination.
About 90 percent of the DNA of the human chromosomes have no known function. Individuals acquire different sequences of this non-functional DNA. They vary in length but consist of sequences of bases, 20-40 bases long, often repeated many times. These unique lengths of DNA, known as hypervariable regions (HVR), are passed on to the offspring and it is this DNA which is used in DNA 'fingerprinting'.
DNA probes have been produced to detect these HVRs at many different loci. The probes developed detect 30-40 different HVRs at once and so the chances of two individuals having the same length is infinitesimally small. The autoradiograph spots reveal a pattern of light and dark bands.

The following information is required without further details of the processes involved.
1. DNA is **separated** from the sample to be tested.
2. **Restriction enzymes** are used to cut up the DNA into sections.
3. The different sized fragments are **separated by electrophoresis**.
4. Radioactive DNA **probes** are used to bind to specific portions of the fragments and these portions are placed next to a sheet of X-ray film (autoradiograph).
5. The radioactive probes expose the film revealing a **pattern** of alternating light and dark bands.

This pattern is unique to individuals and is called **a genetic fingerprint** (DNA profile). The bands in a fingerprint are inherited from both parents and are used to convict criminals but can also be used in paternity suits. To do this, white blood cells are taken from the mother and the possible father. From the pattern of bands of the child are taken away those bands which correspond to the mother's bands. If the man is the true father, he must possess all the remaining bands in the child's genetic fingerprint.

1.7 Cell division

Chromosome structure

The number of chromosomes in the cells of different species varies. Humans always have 46 chromosomes, a mouse has 40 chromosomes. Chromosomes are made up of **DNA**, protein and a small amount of RNA . DNA occurs as a single strand in the form of a double helix running the length of the chromosome. It is only at the onset of cell division that chromosomes become visible. Each chromosome is seen to consists of two threads called **chromatids** that lie parallel along most of their length but are joined only in a specialised region called the **centromere**. The centromere holds the two chromatids together.

Mitosis

Dividing cells undergo a regular pattern of events, known as the **cell cycle**. This is a continuous process but for convenience of description it is subdivided into four stages plus a 'resting' stage, known as interphase, between one complete division.

Interphase
This is the longest part of the cycle during which a newly formed cell increases in size and **produces organelles** lost during the previous division. The amount of **DNA is doubled** during this period. Just before the next cell division the chromosomes replicate so that each then consists of two chromatids joined together by the centromere.

The following are the four stages of mitosis:

Prophase
This is the phase of mitotic division during which the **chromatids shorten and become thicker** by the spiralisation and condensation of the DNA protein coat. In cells where centrioles are present i.e. animals and lower plants, the **centrioles move to the poles of the cells** and microtubules begin to radiate from them forming asters. At the end of prophase the **nuclear membrane disintegrates** and the **spindle is formed**. During this phase the **nucleoli disappear**.

Metaphase
The **chromosomes** arrange themselves at the centre or **equator of the spindle** and become attached to certain spindle fibres at the centromere. Contraction of these fibres draws the individual chromatids slightly apart.

Anaphase
This stage is very rapid. The centromere splits and the **spindle fibres pull the now separated chromatids to the poles** of the cell, where they become the chromosomes of the two daughter cells.

Telophase
Mitosis ends with telophase. The **chromosomes**, having **reached the poles of the cells**, uncoil and lengthen. The **spindle breaks down**, the **centrioles replicate**, the nucleoli reappear and the nuclear **membrane reforms**. In **animal cells cytokinesis** occurs by the constriction of the centre of the parent cell from the outside inwards. In **plant cells, a cell**

plate forms across the equator of the parent cell from the centre outwards and a new cell wall is laid down.

❑ *Action*

1. Make a list of the key words and give their definitions. e.g. **homologous** means that in the diploid cell each chromosome has a partner of exactly the same length and with precisely the same genes.
2. Construct a table summarising the changes that take place at each of the four stages of mitosis.
3. Construct a pie chart showing the relative length of time of each period of the cell cycle.
4. Draw labelled diagrams showing the stages in mitosis.

Significance of mitosis

- Mitosis produces two cells that have the same number of chromosomes as the parent cell and each **chromosome is an exact replica** of one of the originals.
- The division allows the production of cells that are **genetically identical to the parent** and so gives genetic stability.
- By producing new cells, mitosis leads to **growth** of an organism and also allows for **repair** of tissues and the replacement of dead cells.
- An additional function of mitosis is to provide for asexual reproduction, e.g. in bacteria.

Meiosis

Meiosis is the reduction division that occurs during gamete formation in sexually reproducing organisms. In this division the **diploid** number of chromosomes (2n) is reduced to the **haploid** (n).

Usually there are **two cycles** of division:

1. Where the chromosome number is reduced – **meiosis I**
2. Where the two new haploid nuclei divide again in a division identical to that of mitosis – **meiosis II**

The net result is that four haploid nuclei are formed from the parent nucleus.

Like mitosis, meiosis is a gradual process but for convenience it is divided into the four phases of prophase, metaphase, anaphase and telophase, these phases occurring once in each of the two divisions.

Prophase 1

This stage is similar to prophase in mitosis in that the **chromosomes** shorten and fatten and become visible but in meiosis they **associate in their homologous pairs,** and each pair is called a **bivalent.**

At a certain stage in prophase 1 the chromosomes appear double-stranded, as the sister **chromatids** of each chromosome separate and **become visible**. These chromatids wrap around each other and then partially repel each other but remain joined at certain points called **chiasmata.** At these points chromatids may break and recombine with a different but equivalent chromatid. This swapping of pieces of chromosomes is called **crossing over** and is a source of genetic variation.

Metaphase 1

At this stage when the pairs of **homologous chromosomes** arrange themselves on the **equator of the spindle** they do so randomly. This **random distribution** and consequent **independent assortment** of chromosomes produces **new genetic combinations**.

Anaphase 1

Homologous chromosomes are pulled apart and one of each pair is pulled to one pole, its sister chromosome to the opposite pole.
The chromosomes reach the opposite poles and the **nuclear envelope reforms**.

Telophase 1

The nucleus may enter interphase but in some cells this stage does not occur and the cell passes from anaphase 1 directly into prophase II.

Meiosis II is a typical mitotic division and the result is the formation of **four haploid daughter cells**.

❑ *Action*

1. Make a list of the **key words** and give **definitions** e.g. a homologous pair of chromosomes are of the same length and centromere position possessing genes for the same characteristics at corresponding loci. One of the pair is inherited from the father and the other from the mother.
2. Draw **diagrams** of the stages in meiosis.
3. Construct a two-column table using the headings 'stage of meiosis' and 'key process taking place'
4. Recognise the meiotic stages from diagrams, prepared slides and photographs.

Meiosis and variation

In the long term, if a species is to survive in a constantly changing environment and to colonise new environments sources of variation are essential. There are three ways of creating variety:

- Each of the chromosomes making up a homologous pair carries different genetic material. During sexual reproduction the **genotype of one parent is mixed with that of the other** when haploid gametes fuse.
- The different pairs of **homologous chromosomes** arrange themselves on the spindle during metaphase 1 of meiosis. When they subsequently **separate** they do so entirely **independently** of each other, so that the daughter cells contain different combinations of chromosomes.
- **Crossing over** during chiasmata formation during prophase 1 of meiosis. Equivalent parts of homologous chromosomes may be exchanged thus producing new combinations and the separation of linked genes.

❑ *Action*

1. Draw diagrams to illustrate the three ways of creating variety.
2. Construct a table to show the advantages and disadvantages of sexual and asexual reproduction.

2.1 Organisms need transport systems

All living organisms exchange gases with the environment. The raw materials for processes like respiration and photosynthesis must be transported to the cells that need them and waste products must be carried away. Soluble food absorbed by the gut wall of animals must be transported around the body, and the products of photosynthesis must be taken to all parts of the plant. The exchange of materials is carried out passively by diffusion and osmosis and actively by active transport, pinocytosis and phagocytosis.

Overcoming problems associated with increase in size

Living things need to obtain materials such as carbon dioxide and oxygen from the environment and remove waste from their cells to the environment. However, their needs may be proportional to volume whereas diffusion is proportional to surface area.
- In order to achieve the maximum rate of diffusion a respiratory surface must be:
- ✓ **thin** so that diffusion paths are short.
- ✓ **permeable** to the respiratory gases.
- ✓ **moist** to allow easier diffusion of gases.
- ✓ have a sufficiently **large surface area** to satisfy the needs of the organism.
- In simple, **single-celled** organisms, e.g. *Amoeba*, the cell is in contact with water which surrounds it. Diffusion of gases occurs over the whole of the body surface. The large surface area to volume ratio is such that it is large enough to satisfy the organism's needs, the diffusion paths are short and there is no need for a circulatory system.
- Larger, **multicellular** organisms may have a surface area to volume ratio which is too small to supply all their needs, unless they have:
- ✓ modest requirements because they have a very low metabolic rate.
- ✓ become flattened in shape. This considerably increases the surface area to volume ratio and ensures that no part of the body is far from the surface which supplies its nutrients, e.g. flatworms.
- Further increase in size and complexity required the development of specialised exchange surfaces to compensate for the increased oxygen demand. This is because:
- ✓ the surface is some distance from most of the cells.
- ✓ there is an increase in metabolic rate.
- ✓ there is a decrease in surface area to volume ratio.

When large size is combined with a high metabolic rate there is a need for an efficient means of transport as well as specialised exchange surfaces.
- In **water** the exchange surfaces for respiratory gases take the form of **gills**, e.g. fish.
- On **land** vertebrates have developed **lungs.** A lung is a compact respiratory surface, but with a large surface area.

Both gills and lungs need a means of **ventilation** to supply the respiratory surfaces with a fresh supply of oxygen and to maintain diffusion gradients.

With an increase in size and specialisation tissues and organs became more dependent on one another. Materials needed to be exchanged between different organs as well as between the organs and the environment. This is achieved by the development of:
- ✓ **an internal transport system** – provided by a blood circulation system to move gases between respiring cells and the respiratory surface.
- ✓ **a respiratory pigment** in the blood – to increase its oxygen carrying capacity.

2.2 Gas exchange in living organisms

Gaseous exchange in the earthworm

An earthworm is a multicellular, terrestrial animal restricted to damp areas. It is small enough not to require a special surface for gaseous exchange. It is slow moving and this reduces its need for oxygen. It is adapted by having:
- a moist body surface for diffusion.
- a circulatory system and blood pigments.

Gaseous exchange in a bony fish

Bony fish are larger and more active. Water is a dense medium with a low oxygen content and this presents fish with certain difficulties. In fish gaseous exchange takes place across a special surface, the gill, over which a one-way current of water is kept flowing by a specialised pumping mechanism. The density of the water prevents the gills from collapsing and lying on top of each other.

❑ **Action**   1. Draw a diagram of the detailed structure of the gills of a bony fish.
             2. Draw a diagram of a horizontal section through the pharynx and gill region.

Gills consist of a specialised area rather than the whole body surface. They:
- provide a large surface extended by the gill filaments.
- have an extensive network of blood capillaries to allow efficient diffusion and haemoglobin for oxygen carriage.

To increase efficiency water needs to be forced over the gill filaments by pressure differences so maintaining a continuous, unidirectional flow of water. A lower pressure is maintained in the opercular cavity than in the bucco-pharynx. The operculum acts as both a valve, permitting water out, and as a pump drawing water past the gill filaments. The mouth also acts as a pump.

The **ventilation mechanism** for forcing water over the gill filaments operates as follows

mouth	opens
operculum	closed
floor of buccal cavity	lowered
volume	increases
pressure	decreases

water in

Counter current flow

The orientation of the gas-exchange surfaces is such that as the water passes from the pharynx into the opercular chamber, it flows between the gill plates in the opposite direction to the blood flow. This increases efficiency because the diffusion gradient between the adjacent flows is maintained over the whole length of the gill filament, i.e. the blood always meets water with a relatively higher oxygen content.

Gaseous exchange in plants

Plants have a large surface area to capture light. This is provided by the leaves, which also provide a large surface for the exchange of gases. As plants have a low metabolic rate the process of diffusion is adequate for their needs.

(This topic is dealt with in detail on page 38.)

2.2 Gas exchange in mammals

The respiratory surface

In order to achieve the maximum rate of diffusion a respiratory surface must have the following features:

- **thin** so that diffusion paths are short.
- **permeable** to the respiratory gases.
- **moist** to allow easier diffusion of gases.
- a sufficiently **large surface area** to satisfy the needs of the organism.

Gaseous exchange in mammals

Mammals, being relatively large, have a small surface area to volume ratio and often have a higher rate of metabolism than unicellular organisms. They therefore require more oxygen and produce more carbon dioxide. Gases cannot readily penetrate their surface so they, like other multicellular animals, have evolved special gaseous exchange mechanisms. Mammals are active and adapted for exchange with air, a less dense medium, instead of water, so have internal lungs to minimise loss of water and heat.

The structure of the human respiratory system

The lungs are enclosed within an airtight compartment, the **thorax,** at the base of which is a dome-shaped sheet of muscle, called the **diaphragm.** Air is drawn into the lungs via the trachea. The lungs consist of a branching network of tubes called **bronchioles** arising from a pair of **bronchi**.

❑ *Action*   Draw a labelled diagram of the respiratory system.
  You should include the following labelled parts: epiglottis, trachea, bronchi, bronchioles, alveoli, pleural membranes, ribs, intercostal muscles, diaphragm.

Lungs supply a large surface area, increased by alveoli, lined with moisture for dissolving of gases, thin walls to aid diffusion and an extensive capillary network for rapid diffusion and transport, to maintain diffusion gradients.

Ventilation of the lungs

Mammals ventilate their lungs by negative pressure breathing, forcing air down into the lungs:

	Inspiration	Expiration
external intercostal muscle	contracts	relaxes
ribs	up and out	down and in
diaphragm	contracts and flattens	relaxes
volume of thorax	increases	decreases
pressure in thorax	decreases	increases
outside air(atmospheric) pressure	Greater therefore air moves in	Less therefore air moves out

Gas exchange in the alveolus

In the alveoli there is a thin film of moisture in which the oxygen dissolves and then diffuses into the blood capillaries. Carbon dioxide diffuses from the blood into the alveoli.

❑ *Action*   Draw a labelled diagram of a single alveolus.

Measurement of lung capacity

Human lungs have a volume of about 5 dm^3, but at rest only about 0.45 dm^3 of this will be exchanged. This is called **tidal volume**. With increasing activity both the **frequency and depth** of inspiration will increase. **Vital capacity** is the total volume of air that can be expired after a maximum inspiration. Even after maximum expiration about 1.5 dm^3 of air remains in the lungs. This is called the **residual volume.**

In humans a spirometer can be used to record and measure lung volumes and oxygen consumption. You should understand the principles of spirometry and be able to interpret spirometer data in the form of a spirometer trace recorded on a kymograph. However, you are **not** required to carry out practical work using a spirometer.

The rate at which a person breathes is expressed as the **ventilation rate**.
     Ventilation rate   =   tidal volume   x   number of breaths per minute.

❑   *Action*
1. Draw a graph with lung volume (along the vertical axis) against time to show typical human lung volumes based on spirometer readings.
2. Study spirometer traces.
3. Write out a list of terms and their definitions.

Pulmonary disorders

Two pulmonary disorders that affect lung function are asthma and emphysema.
- **Asthma** is a reaction, usually allergic, characterised by attacks of wheezing and difficulty in breathing. Attacks are brought on by **spasms of the smooth muscles** that lie in the walls of the smaller bronchi and bronchioles, **causing the passageways to close partially**. Usually the mucous membranes that line the respiratory passageways become irritated and secrete excessive amounts of mucus that may clog the bronchi and bronchioles and worsen the attack.
- **Emphysema** develops over a period of about 20 years and is impossible to diagnose until the lungs have been irreversibly damaged. In the early stages the only symptom is breathlessness but as this gets progressively worse the sufferer becomes so disabled that they cannot even get out of bed.
  In emphysema the **walls of the alveoli lose their elasticity** and remain filled with air during expiration. As the condition progresses the walls of the **alveoli break down** and many alveoli may merge to form larger air sacs with a **reduced overall volume**. The lungs become permanently inflated because they have lost their elasticity. Little, if any, exchange of gases can take place across the stretched and damaged air sacs.
  Emphysema is generally caused by long-term irritation. Air pollution, occupational exposure to industrial dust, and cigarette smoke are the most common irritants. Cigarette smoke not only deactivates a protein crucial in preventing emphysema but also prevents the repair of affected lung tissue. Emphysema cannot be cured and the disease cannot be reversed. The only way to minimise the chance of getting it is not to smoke at all or to give up smoking. If you smoke the chances are that some damage has already been done. However giving up can significantly reduce the rate of further deterioration.

In humans a natural surfactant is present which lowers the surface tension so keeping the alveoli open.
A surfactant may be used to treat babies born prematurely before their own lungs secrete the surfactant.

2.2 Gas exchange in plants

The leaf as an organ of gaseous exchange

The structure of the leaves of flowering plants is related to their function of gaseous exchange.

To enable gaseous exchange to take place efficiently:
- the lamina(leaf blade) is thin so diffusion paths for gases are short.
- the spongy mesophyll tissue allows for the circulation of gases.
- the plant tissues are permeated by air spaces.
- the stomatal pores permit gas exchange.
- leaves have a large surface area to volume ratio.

- ❑ *Action*   Draw a labelled diagram of T.S. angiosperm leaf.
                You should include the following labels: cuticle, epidermis, palisade mesophyll, spongy mesophyll, vascular bundle, air space, stomata, guard cells.

Gases diffuse through the stomata along the concentration gradient. Once inside the leaf the gases in the sub-stomatal air chambers diffuse through the intercellular spaces between the mesophyll cells and diffuse into the cells. The direction of diffusion depends on the environmental conditions and the requirements of the plants. It is the net exchange of carbon dioxide and oxygen in relation to respiration and photosynthesis that matters.

Adaptations of the leaf for photosynthesis

To ensure the efficient absorption of light the leaf shows the following adaptations:
- Leaves have a large surface area to capture as much sunlight as possible.
- Leaves can orientate themselves so that they are held at an angle perpendicular to the sun during the day to expose the maximum area to the light.
- Leaves are thin to allow light to penetrate the lower layers of cells.
- The cuticle and epidermis are transparent to allow light to penetrate to the mesophyll.
- Palisade cells are elongated and densely arranged in a layer, or layers.
- The palisade cells are packed with chloroplasts and arranged with their long axes perpendicular to the surface.
- The chloroplasts can rotate and move within the mesophyll cells. This allows them to arrange themselves into the best positions for the efficient absorption of light.
- The intercellular air spaces in the spongy mesophyll allow carbon dioxide to diffuse to the cells and oxygen can diffuse away.

Stomata

- Leaves have a cuticle to prevent water loss. However, the cuticle also reduces gaseous exchange.
- This is overcome by the presence of stomata, which allow water and gases through.
- Stomata are pores in the epidermis, each bordered by two guard cells. The guard cells differ from the other epidermal cells in that they possess chloroplasts. The inner wall of each guard cell is thicker than the outer wall.
- Guard cells around the stomata can change shape to open and close the stomata so helping to control gas exchange and water loss.
- An inevitable result of the necessity for the inside of the leaf to be open to the atmosphere for the exchange of gases is that water is lost from the leaves by the process of transpiration. In conditions of water deficit the stomata close.

The opening and closing mechanism of stomata

Guard cells change shape because of changes in turgor.
In the light, water flows in by osmosis so the cells expand. The inner wall is inelastic so the pairs of cells curve away from each other and the pore opens.

❑ **Action**   Draw labelled diagrams of stomata in the open and closed states.

During the day the mechanism for stomatal opening occurs as follows:
- a potassium ion (K^+) pump in the cell membranes actively transports K^+ ions into the guard cells.
- as photosynthesis occurs the carbon dioxide concentration falls.
- the pH rises and an enzyme catalyses the conversion of starch to malate.
- K^+ and malate ions accumulate in guard cells.
- the WP is lowered and water flows in by osmosis.
- guard cells become turgid and curve apart more because their outer walls are thinner than the inner walls, so the pore widens.

At night pores close due to the reverse process.

❑ **Action**   Describe the mechanism for stomatal closure.

Xerophytes are plants that have adapted to living under conditions of low water availability. They have   modified structures to prevent excessive water loss (see page 42).
Xerophytes may open stomata at night instead of during the day in order to conserve water, whilst other plants may close stomata during the day or night under drought conditions.

2.3a   Transport in plants

In plants the organs collecting the water, the roots, are some distance from the leaves, which require the water for the process of photosynthesis. A transport system through the stem is necessary to connect the two organs.

Vascular tissues

The vascular tissues are made up of:
- the **xylem,** which transports water and mineral salts from the roots to the leaves.
- the **phloem,** which transports the soluble products of photosynthesis from the leaves to the other parts of the plant.

Structure of xylem

Xylem is made up of four different types of cells:
- **vessels**
- **tracheids**
- **fibres**
- **xylem parenchyma**

Vessels and tracheids are the cells involved in **conduction**. These are dead cells and they form a system of tubes through which water can travel. The cells are dead because **lignin** has been deposited on the cellulose cell walls rendering them impermeable to water and solutes. These cells also provide mechanical strength and support to the plant.

Xylem distribution

The distribution of xylem tissue differs in primary stems, leaves and roots.
- In **stems** it occurs as part of the peripheral vascular bundles. This organisation gives flexible support, but also resistance to bending strain.
- In **leaves** the arrangement of vascular tissues in the midrib and network of veins also gives flexible strength and resistance to tearing strains.
- In **roots** the central arrangement is ideal for resistance to pull and so helps the anchorage of the plant.

❑   *Action*   1.   Draw T.S. and L.S. diagrams of primary phloem.
                  2.   Draw labelled diagrams of T.S. dicotyledon primary stem.
                  3.   Draw labelled diagrams of T.S. dicotyledon primary root.

Water uptake by the roots

The large quantities of water lost through transpiration must be replaced from the soil. The region of greatest uptake is the root hair zone where the surface area of the root is enormously increased by the presence of root hairs from the cells of the piliferous layer. Water can travel across the root along three pathways:
- the **apoplast** – through the cell wall.
- the **symplast** – through the cytoplasm and plasmodesmata.
- the **vacuolar pathway** – from vacuole to vacuole.

✓   Most of the water enters the root, from the soil, down a gradient of water potential. It then passes across the root cortex along two main pathways, the symplast and apoplast pathways. Most of the water probably follows the latter pathway as this is the faster of the two.

✓ A layer of cells called the **endodermis** surrounds the pericycle within which lies the vascular tissue (stele). The cells of the endodermis have layers of suberin around them, forming a distinctive band known as the **Casparian strip**. The suberin is waterproof and prevents the use of the apoplast pathway. Thus the water passes across the plasma membrane and continues across the symplast pathway, the only available route to the xylem.

✓ When the water reaches the cells of the pericycle it is transferred to the apoplast pathway before entering the xylem tissue. This is because the xylem cells lack cell contents.

There is some evidence that salts may then be actively secreted into the vascular tissue from the endodermal cells. This makes the WP in the xylem more negative, causing water to be drawn in from the endodermis, so promoting the movement of water into the xylem from the cortex. The water potential gradient created produced creates a force known as the **root pressure**.

The uptake of minerals

Generally, minerals are taken up by the root hairs by **active transport** from the soil solution. Once absorbed the mineral ions may move along the apoplast pathway carried along in solution by the water being pulled up the plant in the transpiration stream. When minerals reach the endodermis the Casparian strip prevents further movement along the cell walls. The ions enter the cytoplasm of the cell from where they diffuse or are actively transported into the xylem. E.g. nitrogen usually enters the plant as nitrate ions/ammonium ions which diffuse along the concentration gradient into the apoplast stream but enter symplast by active transport against the concentration gradient and then flow via plasmodesmata in the cytoplasmic stream.

At the endodermis ions must be actively taken up to by-pass the Casparian band which allows the plant to selectively take up the ions at this point.

The movement of water from the root to the leaf

- Water travels in the xylem up through the stem to the leaves, where most of it evaporates from the internal leaf surface and passes out, as water vapour, into the atmosphere.
- The transpiration of water from the leaves draws water across the leaf from the xylem tissue along three same pathways as in the root.
- As water molecules leave xylem cells in the leaf, they pull up other water molecules. This pulling effect is known as the **transpiration pull** and is possible because of the large **cohesive** forces between water molecules and the **adhesive** forces which exist between the water molecules and the walls of the vessels. These two forces combine to maintain the column of water in the xylem.
- The theory of the mechanism by which water moves up the xylem is known as the **Cohesion-Tension theory**.

Transpiration

About 99% of the water moving through the plant is lost from the leaves as water vapour. This evaporation of water from inside the leaves through the stomata to the atmosphere is known as transpiration and gives rise to the **transpiration stream**. The continued removal of water molecules from the top of the xylem vessels results in a tension causing a pull on the xylem column.

The rate at which water is lost from plants is called the **transpiration rate** and is dependent on external factors such as **temperature, humidity** and **air movement**. .Any factor that increases the water potential gradient between the water vapour in the leaf and the surrounding atmosphere increases the rate of transpiration.

- **Temperature** – a rise in temperature provides additional kinetic energy for the movement of water molecules. This additional energy accelerates the rate of evaporation of water from the walls of the mesophyll cells and, if the stomata are open, speeds up the rate of diffusion of water vapour into the surrounding atmosphere. The water potential of the atmosphere becomes lower as its temperature is raised and it can hold more moisture.
- **Humidity** – the air inside a leaf is saturated with water vapour but the humidity of the atmosphere surrounding a leaf varies, with values exceeding 70% being rare in Britain. Thus the water potential gradient between leaf and atmosphere is always great and when the stomata are open water vapour rapidly diffuses from the leaf.
- **Air movement** – transpiration in still air results in the accumulation of a layer of saturated air at the surfaces of leaves. This offers considerable resistance to the diffusion of water vapour through stomata and thus reduces the rate of transpiration. Movement of the surrounding air reduces the thickness of the layer of saturated air and results in increased transpiration.

Light intensity also affects transpiration by controlling the degree of stomatal opening.

❑ *Action*   1. Draw graphs showing how environmental factors affect the rate of transpiration.
       2. Make sure you know how to use a simple potometer.

In reality, these **factors** do not act independently but **interact** with each other, e.g. More water is lost on a dry, windy day than on a humid, still day. This is because the sub-stomatal chamber has a high water potential as the walls of the spongy mesophyll cells are saturated with water. The water evaporates from the walls and moves down a gradient of water potential from the plant to the atmosphere which has a low % relative humidity; the wind having reduced the thickness of the layer of saturated air at the leaf surface.

Xerophytes

Plants growing in normal soil with a relatively constant supply of water are referred to as mesophytes. Most land plants growing in temperate regions belong to this category. Usually the water that they lose by transpiration is readily replaced by uptake from the soil, so they do not require any special means of conserving water. If such a plant loses too much water the plant wilts and the leaves droop. The leaf surface area is reduced and photosynthesis becomes less efficient.

Some plants exhibit **xeromorphic** adaptations and are known as **xerophytes**. Xerophytes have adapted to living under conditions of low water availability so have modified structures to prevent excessive water loss. They may live in:
- hot, dry desert regions.
- cold regions where the soil water is frozen for much of the year.
- exposed, windy situations.

You are required to study *Ammophila arenaria* (**marram grass**), which colonises sand dunes around the coast. The sand dune habitat makes it difficult for a mesophyte to survive there because there is no soil, rapid drainage of rain water occurs, there are high wind speeds, salt spray and a lack of shade from the sun.

❑ *Action*   Draw, label and annotate diagram of T.S. leaf of marram grass.

Marram grass shows the following modifications:
- **Rolled leaves** – large thin-walled epidermal cells at the bases of the furrows shrink when they lose water from excessive transpiration, causing the leaf to roll onto itself. This has the effect of reducing the leaf area from which transpiration can occur.
- **Sunken stomata** – stomata only occur on the furrows on the inner side of the leaf. They are located in pits or depressions so that moist air is trapped outside the stomata. This reduces the water potential gradient between the leaf and the atmosphere and so reduces the rate of diffusion of water.
- **Hairs** – stiff, interlocking hairs trap moist air and reduce the water potential gradient.
- **Thick cuticle** – the cuticle is a waxy covering over the leaf surface which reduces water loss. The thicker this cuticle the lower the rate of cuticular transpiration.

2.3a Translocation

The products of photosynthesis are transported in the phloem, away from the site of synthesis (the 'source') in the leaves, to all the other parts of the plant (the 'sink') where they are used for growth or storage. In plants the transport of the soluble organic materials, sucrose and amino acids, is known as translocation.

Structure of phloem

Phloem is a living tissue and consists of four types of cells:
- **sieve tubes**
- **companion cells**
- **phloem fibres**
- **phloem parenchyma**

The sieve tubes are the only components of phloem obviously adapted for the longitudinal flow of material. They are formed from cells called sieve elements placed end to end. The end walls do not break down but are perforated by pores. These areas are known as **sieve plates**. Cytoplasmic filaments containing phloem protein extend from one sieve cell to the next through the pores in the sieve plate. The sieve tubes do not possess a nucleus and most of the other cell organelles disintegrate. Each sieve tube element is closely associated with at least one companion cell, which have dense cytoplasm, large centrally placed nuclei, many mitochondria, and they are connected to the sieve tube element by **plasmodesmata**.

❑ *Action*   1. Draw T.S. and L.S. of primary phloem.
                 2. Observe structure of phloem as seen under the electron microscope.

Transport in the phloem

The observed rate of flow is much too rapid for diffusion to be the cause. The main theory put forward to explain the transport of organic solutes is known as the **mass flow hypothesis** (put forward in 1937 by Ernst Munch). This theory suggests that there is a passive mass flow of sugars from the phloem of the leaf where there is the highest concentration (the source) to other areas, such as growing tissues, where there is a lower concentration (the sink).

- At the source phloem companion cells actively take up sugars and pass them to the sieve tubes while the reverse process occurs at the sink. Transfer cells, which occur in the mesophyll, are found associated with the phloem tissue and are thought to be involved in this process.
- This causes a concentration gradient from source to sink.
- Water is drawn in by osmosis, setting up a hydrostatic pressure resulting in movement of sugar to the sink.
- At the sink the sugar concentration decreases, as it is used for metabolic processes, so water passes out into the tissues.
- The continual input of sugars and water at the top of the system and their removal at the bottom creates a pressure gradient which maintains the downward flow of fluid in the sieve tubes.

There are **drawbacks to the mass flow hypothesis**. These include:
✓ it does not explain the existence of the sieve plates which seemingly act as a series of barriers impeding flow.

44

✓ sugars and amino acids have been observed to move at different rates and in different directions in the same tissue.

Other hypotheses have been proposed. These include diffusion and cytoplasmic streaming along the protein filaments. (You are not required to provide details of these.)

❏ **Action**   Draw a model to explain the principle of the mass flow hypothesis.

2.3b   The human circulatory system

Multicellular animals have a transport system which **in mammals** consists of a circulatory system made up of a closed, double circulation and a heart with two atria and two ventricles. The transport system thus incorporates a **pump** to sustain high pressure, **valves** to control the flow and **vessels** to distribute the blood.

Blood vessels and the circulation system

Blood is pumped by the heart into thick-walled vessels called **arteries.** These split up into smaller vessels called arterioles, from which the blood passes into the **capillaries**. The capillaries form a vast network which penetrates all the tissues and organs of the body. Blood from the capillaries collects into venules, which in turn empty blood into **veins**, from which it is returned to the heart.

❑ ***Action***   Draw and label a general plan of the circulatory system in the human.
(You are required only to name the main blood vessels associated with the heart.)

Structure and function of blood vessels

The **arteries** and the **veins** have the same basic three-layered structure but the proportions of the different layers do vary. In both:
- the innermost layer is the **endothelium**, which is one cell thick and provides a smooth lining to reduce friction and provide a minimum resistance to the flow of the blood.
- the middle layer is made up of **elastic fibres** and **smooth muscle**. This layer is thicker in the arteries than in the veins to accommodate changes in blood flow and pressure as blood is pumped from the heart.
- the outer layer is made up of **collagen fibres** which are resistant to over-stretching.

Veins have larger diameters and thinner walls than arteries as the pressure and flow is reduced.
Veins have semi-lunar **valves** along their length to ensure flow in one direction(prevent back flow); these are not present in arteries apart from the aortic valves.

The **capillaries** are thin walled, consisting only of a layer of endothelium so their walls are permeable to water and dissolved substances such as glucose. It is at the capillaries that the exchange of materials between the blood and the tissues takes place. As the capillaries are small they have a large cross-sectional area and this restricts the flow of blood. It is important that blood velocity slows in capillary beds to allow time for the transfer of materials between the blood and the tissue fluid (see page 51).
(It may at first seem that the blood should travel faster through capillaries than through arteries, because the diameters of the capillaries are much smaller. However, it is the *total* cross sectional area delivering the blood that determines the flow rate.)

❑ ***Action***   1. Draw labelled diagrams of an artery, vein and capillary.
2. Construct a detailed table comparing arteries and veins.

2.3b The heart

A pump to circulate blood is an essential feature of a circulatory system. The heart consists of a thin walled collection chamber and a thick walled pumping chamber which are partitioned into two, allowing the complete separation of oxygenated and deoxygenated blood.

The heart

The heart is situated in the thorax between the two lungs.
- The heart is four-chambered, and
- consists largely of **cardiac** muscle, a specialised tissue that is capable of rhythmical contraction and relaxation over a long period without fatigue.

❏ *Action*   Draw a labelled diagram of the mammalian heart as seen in vertical section.

Blood flow through the heart

The following describes blood flow through the left side of the heart:
- The **left atrium** is relaxed and receives oxygenated blood from the **pulmonary vein**.
- When full the pressure forces open the **bicuspid valve** between the atrium and ventricle.
- Relaxation of the **left ventricle** draws blood from the left atrium.
- The left atrium contracts pushing the remaining blood into the right ventricle through the valve.
- With the left atrium relaxed and with the bicuspid valve closed the left ventricle contracts.
- The strong muscular walls exert a strong pressure and push blood away from the heart through the semi-lunar valves through the pulmonary arteries and the aorta.

- Both sides of the heart work together i.e. both ventricles contract at the same time, both atria contract together. One complete contraction and relaxation is called a heartbeat.
- After contraction, and the compartment has been emptied of blood, it relaxes, to be filled with blood once more.
- The ventricles are made of more muscle than the atria and so generate more pressure to force the blood a greater distance.
- The left ventricle has a thicker muscular wall than the right ventricle as it has to pump the blood all round the body whereas the right ventricle has only to pump the blood a shorter distance to the lungs.

Pressure changes
- The highest pressure occurs in the aorta/arteries that show a rhythmic rise and fall corresponding to ventricular contraction.
- Friction with vessel walls causes a progressive drop in pressure. Arterioles have large total surface area and a relatively narrow bore causing a substantial reduction from aortic pressure. Their pressure depends on whether they are dilated or contracted.
- The extensive capillary beds have a large cross sectional area. These beds create an even greater resistance to blood flow.
- There is a relationship between pressure and speed and the pressure drops further due to leakage from capillaries into tissues.

- The return flow to the heart is non-rhythmic and the pressure in the veins is low but can be increased by the massaging effect of muscles.

- ❏ *Action*   1. Draw labelled diagrams to illustrate the cardiac cycle.
  2. Describe the flow of blood through the right side of the heart.

Control of heartbeat

The heart muscle is **myogenic** i.e. the heartbeat is initiated from within the muscle itself and is not due to nervous stimulation.
- In the wall of the right atrium is a region of specialised cardiac fibres called the **sinoatrial node** (SAN) which acts as a **pacemaker**.
- A wave of electrical stimulation arises at this point and then spreads over the two atria causing them to contract more or less at the same time.
- The electrical stimulation is prevented from spreading to the ventricles by a thin layer of connective tissue.
- The stimulation reaches another specialised region of cardiac fibres, the **atrio–ventricular node** (AVN), which lies between the two atria and which passes on the excitation to specialised tissues in the ventricles.
- From the AVN the excitation passes along the **bundle of His** and then spreads through the **Purkinje tissue** in the walls of the ventricles.
- The contraction of the ventricles is therefore delayed after the atria.
- As with the atria, stimulation is followed by contraction and the walls of the ventricle contract simultaneously.

- ❏ *Action*   Draw a labelled diagram of a vertical section through the heart to show the position of the sino-atrial node, atrio-ventricular node and the bundle of His.

Heart rate

- The human heart normally contracts 70 times a minute, but this can be varied from 50 to 200 times a minute.
- The volume of blood pumped at each beat can also be varied.
  - Cardiac output = volume pumped x number of beats in a given time
- Changes to the cardiac output are effected through the autonomic nervous system.
- ✓ stimulation of the **vagus nerve** will slow down the heartbeat.
- ✓ stimulation of the **sympathetic nerve** will accelerate it.

The cardiac centre of the brain originates the sympathetic and parasympathetic impulses.

2.3b Blood and the transport of materials

In mammals a transport system provides the link between specialised areas for gas exchange and the cells which require oxygen and nutrients. As all cells are bathed in an aqueous medium, the delivery of materials to and from these cells is carried out largely in solution. The fluid in which the materials are dissolved or suspended is blood.

Composition of blood

Blood is a tissue made up of **cells** in a fluid **plasma**.
- **plasma** is made up largely of 90% water, with soluble food molecules, waste products, hormones, plasma proteins, mineral ions and vitamins dissolved in it.
- **blood cells** are of three types:
- ✓ erythrocytes or red blood corpuscles.
- ✓ leucocytes or white blood corpuscles.
- ✓ thrombocytes or platelets.

Functions of blood

- Plasma – **transports** digested food products, hormones, proteins, fibrinogen, antibodies etc. and also distributes heat.
- Erythrocytes – these are filled with the pigment haemoglobin, are biconcave in shape and do not contain a nucleus. Their function is the **carriage of oxygen** and this process is carried out as described below.
- Leucocytes – these are of two groups:
- ✓ granulocytes, which are **phagocytic**, have granular cytoplasm, lobed nuclei and **engulf** bacteria.
- ✓ agranulocytes, which produce **antibodies** and **antitoxins**, have clear cytoplasm and spherical nuclei.
- thrombocytes – these are involved in **blood clotting**.
(In this unit you are required to study the functions of red blood cells and plasma only.)

The transport of oxygen

- An efficient respiratory pigment readily picks up oxygen at the respiratory surface and releases it on arrival at the tissues. Respiratory pigments have a high affinity for oxygen when the concentration is high but this is reduced when the concentration is low. Oxygen concentration is measured by partial pressure, known as the **oxygen tension**.
- ✓ Normal atmospheric pressure   = 100 kiloPascals.
- ✓ Oxygen tension (partial pressure) =   21 kiloPascals
  (as oxygen makes up approximately 21% of the atmosphere).
- When the respiratory pigment **haemoglobin** is exposed to a gradual increase in oxygen tension it absorbs oxygen rapidly at first but more slowly as the tension continues to rise. This relationship is known as the **oxygen dissociation curve**.

- ❏ *Action*   Draw the oxygen dissociation curve for adult human haemoglobin.

- The more the dissociation curve of haemoglobin is displaced to the right, the less readily it picks up oxygen, but the more easily it releases it.
- The more the dissociation curve of haemoglobin is displaced to the left, the more readily it picks up oxygen, but the less readily it releases it.

The release of oxygen from haemoglobin is facilitated by the presence of carbon dioxide, a phenomenon known as the **Bohr effect**:

- when the **partial pressure of oxygen is high**, as in the lung capillaries, oxygen combines with the haemoglobin to form **oxyhaemoglobin**.
- when the **partial pressure of oxygen is low**, as found in the respiring tissues, then the oxygen dissociates from the haemoglobin.
- when the **partial pressure of carbon dioxide is high**, haemoglobin is less efficient at taking up oxygen and more efficient at releasing it.

The dissociation curve of foetal haemoglobin
To enable the foetal haemoglobin to absorb oxygen from the maternal haemoglobin in the placenta the foetus has a haemoglobin that differs in two of the four polypeptide chains from the haemoglobin of the adult. This gives the foetal haemoglobin a dissociation curve to the left of that of the adult and therefore a greater affinity for oxygen.

The dissociation curve of Llama haemoglobin
With increase in altitude there is a drop in atmospheric pressure. This is significant for animals, such as the llama, because the partial pressure of oxygen in the atmosphere is less at high altitude.
To compensate for this:

- the llama possesses haemoglobin which loads more readily with oxygen in the lungs. Haemoglobin of this sort has a dissociation curve to the left of normal haemoglobin.
- the number of red cells in the blood of mammals increases.

❑ *Action*   1. Draw the oxygen dissociation curves for foetal haemoglobin.
                2. Draw the oxygen dissociation curves for the llama.

Transport of carbon dioxide

Carbon dioxide is transported in blood cells and plasma in 3 ways:

- 5% in solution in the plasma. (This is inadequate to meet the needs of most organisms.)
- 85% as hydrogencarbonate.
- 10% in combination with haemoglobin to form carbamino-haemoglobin.
  The following describes a series of reactions known as the **chloride shift**:
- ✓ Carbon dioxide diffuses into the red blood cell (RBC) and combines with water to form **carbonic acid**.
- ✓ Carbonic acid dissociates into H^+ and HCO_3^- ions, the reaction being catalysed by **carbonic anhydrase**.
- ✓ HCO_3^- ions diffuse out of the RBC into the plasma where they combine with Na^+ ions from the dissociation of sodium chloride to form sodium hydrogen carbonate.
- ✓ H^+ ions provide the conditions for the **oxyhaemoglobin** to dissociate into oxygen and haemoglobin.
- ✓ H^+ ions are buffered by their combination with haemoglobin and the formation of **haemoglobinic acid** (HHb).
- ✓ The oxygen diffuses out of the RBC into the tissues.
- ✓ to balance the outward movement of negatively charged ions, **chloride ions** diffuse in.
- ✓ This is known as the **chloride shift** and it is by this means that the **electrochemical neutrality** of the RBC is maintained.

❑ *Action*   By means of a diagram or flowchart summarise the main chemical events that take place in a red blood cell on reaching the tissues.

2.3b Intercellular fluid and lymph

- The **capillaries** are the site of exchange between the blood and the cells of the body. The blood is contained in a closed system but fluid derived from plasma escapes through the capillary walls.
  This fluid is called **tissue fluid** and it bathes the cells.

  Tissue fluid = plasma minus proteins.
- Exchange takes place in the capillary beds by pressure filtration caused by the net difference between hydrostatic pressure (forcing liquid out) and osmotic forces (holding liquid in).
- When blood reaches the arterial end of a capillary it is under pressure because of the pumping action of the heart and the resistance to blood flow of the capillaries. This **hydrostatic pressure** forces the fluid part of the blood through the capillary walls into the spaces between the cells.
- This outward flow is opposed by the reduced **water potential** of the blood, created by the presence of the plasma proteins.
- The hydrostatic pressure of the blood is greater than the osmotic forces so there is a net flow of water out of the blood. (As water passes through the capillary wall it carries solutes with it.)
- Oxygen, glucose, amino acids, fatty acids, hormones and inorganic ions contained in tissue fluid are required by the cells of the body.
- At the arterial end of the capillary bed the diffusion gradient for solutes such as glucose, oxygen and ions favours movement from the capillaries to the tissue fluid. This is because these substances are being used during cell metabolism.
- At the venous end of the capillary bed the blood pressure is lower and water passes into the capillaries by osmosis. The reduced water potential of the blood created by the presence of the plasma proteins causes a net inflow of water.
- At the venous end tissue fluid picks up CO_2 and other excretory substances. Some of this fluid passes back into the capillaries, but some drains into the lymphatic system and is returned eventually to the venous system via the thoracic duct which empties into a vein near the heart.

The effect of low blood proteins
Low blood proteins affect capillary filtration and may result in fluid retention in tissues. Receiving the right amount of protein is a particular problem in those parts of the world with large populations and livestock is scarce, e.g. the diet of many African natives consists largely of cornmeal, which does not provide some of the essential amino acids. As a result many African children develop a **protein deficiency disorder** called **kwashiorkor**, one of the symptoms of which is **oedema**. This is a condition where tissue fluid is formed faster than it can be removed. Fluid accumulates in the tissues and the tissues swell up. A child suffering from kwashiorkor is also physically weak and shows retarded growth.

❑ *Action*   1. Draw and annotate a diagram showing the formation and fate of tissue fluid.
  2. Describe how a deficiency of proteins in the diet causes oedema.

(The lymphatic system is studied in unit BI 4 and the following is for information only.)
Lymph is the tissue fluid that drains into blind-ending lymphatic capillaries amongst the tissues. The lymph moves through vessels by contractions of the muscles through which the vessels pass. Lymph glands and nodes associated with the lymph vessels play an important role in the formation of lymphocytes and the prevention of infection.)

2.4 Ecosystems

An **ecosystem** is a natural unit of living (biotic) components in a given area, as well as the non-living (abiotic) factors with which they interact.
There are two main areas of study within an ecosystem:
- The flow of energy through the system.
- The cycling of matter within the system.

Components of an ecosystem

- A **population** is a group of organism of a single species occupying a particular area. In this area there will also be other populations, forming a **community**.
- A **habitat** is the particular area occupied by a population. It has biotic and abiotic features which separate it from other habitats.
- ✓ the biotic features are the sum total of the organisms within the habitat and their interactions.
- ✓ abiotic features include different types:
- ▪ Edaphic features relate to the soil and include all its physical and chemical characteristics.
- ▪ Climatic features include light, temperature, moisture, salinity, and, particularly, the stability or variability of these.
- Microhabitats are small localities within a habitat, each with its own particular conditions.
- Ecological niche is the place of each species in an ecosystem. This is not only the physical space which it occupies, but the role which it carries out within the community and its inter-relationships with other species as well. In the long term, two species cannot occupy the same niche in a specific habitat.

- ❏ *Action*   Give examples of ecosystems, habitats, populations and communities.

Types of nutrition

Nutrition is the process by which organisms obtain **energy** to maintain life functions and **matter** to create and maintain structure. These are obtained from nutrients.
Most **autotrophic** organisms use the simple organic materials, carbon dioxide and water, to manufacture energy-containing complex organic compounds, whereas **heterotrophic** organisms consume complex organic food material.

Autotrophic nutrition

There are two types of autotrophic nutrition:
- **Photosynthesis** – is the process by which green plants, algae and certain types of bacteria build up **complex organic molecules** from carbon dioxide, water, and mineral ions. The source of **energy** for this process comes from **sunlight** which is absorbed by **chlorophyll** and related pigments.
- **Chemosynthesis** – is the process by which a few bacteria can perform similar synthesis of organic compounds using energy derived from special methods of respiration.

Heterotrophic nutrition

Heterotrophic organisms consume complex organic food material.
There are a number of different forms of heterotrophic nutrition.

- **Holozoic**

This involves taking in complex organic molecules, breaking them down by digestion, absorption into the body tissues from the digestive system and finally, utilisation of the absorbed products of digestion in the body cells. Animals that feed solely on plant material are termed **herbivores**, those that feed on other animals are **carnivores**, and the **omnivores** have a mixed diet.

- **Saprobiontic**

This is also known as saprotrophic or saprophytic.
This involves the consumption of complex organic food from the bodies of **decaying** organisms. Some bacteria and fungi feed in this way. They secrete enzymes on the food substrate and then absorb the products of this **extracellular digestion**. The activities of these organisms are important in the decomposition of leaf litter and the recycling of valuable nutrients.

- **Parasitism**

A parasite is an organism which lives in or on another living organism, the **host**. The parasite derives all its nutrition from the host, whereas the host does not gain any benefit from the association and is often harmed to some degree. Some parasites live on the outside of the host, the **ectoparasites** e.g. leech. Others live entirely within the body of the host and are termed **endoparasites** e.g. *Plasmodium,* the malarial parasite. Parasites are considered to be very highly specialised organisms and show considerable adaptations to their mode of life.

- **Mutualism**

This is also known as symbiosis.
This also involves a close association between members of two species, but in this case both derive some benefit from the relationship e.g. the digestion of cellulose by microorganisms in the gut of a herbivore.

Food chains and food webs

The sun's energy is passed from one feeding level (or trophic level) to another through the ecosystem. Energy is passed along a hierarchy of trophic levels with primary producers at the bottom and consumers at the top. This is referred to as a food chain.
The following diagram shows a typical food chain:

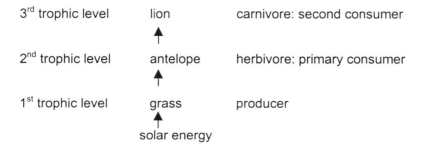

3rd trophic level	lion	carnivore: second consumer
2nd trophic level	antelope	herbivore: primary consumer
1st trophic level	grass	producer
	solar energy	

- Single food chains rarely exist and a food web is a more realistic representation of feeding relationships. This is because most primary consumers feed on more than one kind of autotroph and most secondary consumers rely on more than one type of prey. The more varied the organisms in an environment, the more complex the food web.
- Green plants which manufacture sugars from simple raw materials using solar energy are called **primary producers**.
- Animals feeding on these plants are called **herbivores** or **primary consumers**.
- Animals feeding on these animals are called **carnivores** or **secondary and tertiary consumers**.

❑ *Action*   Make a list of key words with their definitions.

You should be able to:
Draw up food webs given appropriate data.
Predict the effect on food webs when an organism is removed or its numbers increased.

2.4 Energy flow

The study of the flow of energy through the ecosystem is known as ecological energetics.

- Photosynthesis is the source of energy for the ecosystem.
- Producers are the green plants which trap solar energy and manufacture sugars from simple raw materials.
- Herbivores (primary consumers) are animals which feed on plants. Carnivores are animals that feed on other animals.
- Each of these groups forms a feeding or trophic level with energy passing from each level to a higher one as material is eaten.
- Only a small amount of the total energy that reaches the plant as light is incorporated into plant tissues. As energy is passed along the food chain there is a large loss at each level.
- At each level energy is lost through respiration, and in waste products, so the amount of energy is reduced.
- The sequence from plant to herbivore to carnivore is a food chain and is the route by which energy passes between trophic levels.
- It is the loss of energy at each level which limits the length of a food chain so the number of links in a chain is normally limited to four or five.
- On the death of producers and consumers, some energy remains locked up in the organic compounds of which they are made. **Decomposers** and **detritivores** feed as saprobionts and contribute to the recycling of nutrients.
- ✓ **Decomposers** are microbes that obtain nutrients from dead organisms, faeces e.g. by extracellular digestion; bacteria and fungi.
- ✓ **Detritivores** are organisms which feed on small fragments of organic debris from plants and animals, e.g. earthworms. (Detritus is made up of non-living organic material, such as faeces, fallen leaves and the remains of dead organisms.)

- ❏ *Action*   Make a list and give definitions for all the key terms.

Energy source

- The ultimate source of energy for ecosystems is the sun, from which energy is released in the form of electromagnetic waves.
- A good deal of the solar energy reaching the earth's atmosphere does not penetrate it. It is reflected or absorbed and radiated back into space by the ozone layer, dust particles and clouds.
- Also about 90% of the energy getting to the surface of the earth is reflected by vegetation, soil, and water or absorbed and radiated to the earth's atmosphere as heat.
- This means that only about 10% is left for producers to make use of. Therefore, only a small part of the total amount of energy reaching the earth's atmosphere enters ecosystems. Also, the quantity absorbed by plants varies considerably at different latitudes.
- Of the energy entering a plant only 1% to 5% is utilised by the plant, the rest is lost, partly by reflection and partly by the evaporation of water.

Trophic efficiency

This is the percentage of energy at one trophic level which is incorporated into the next trophic level. The rate at which energy passes into the animals at each trophic level is about 10% of that entering the previous level. This is called the **gross ecological efficiency**. This value differs from one ecosystem to another with some of the highest values, around 40%, occurring in oceanic food chains. Some of the lowest values, around 1%, are found in ecosystems where most of the animals are birds or mammals.

Example:
In a particular food chain, if 15000kJ of energy enters the primary consumer level and 1500kJ passes to the secondary consumer level, then:

$$\frac{15000}{1500} \times 100 = 10\% \text{ (This is the gross ecological efficiency.)}$$

Energy flow

The energy flowing from one organism to another in the food chain is not recycled but lost as heat and so it must constantly be replaced by sunlight reaching the earth.
If it is assumed that 100 units of energy per unit time reach the leaves of a crop plant:

Units of energy	What happens to the energy?
50	the 'wrong' wavelength i.e. the photosynthetic pigments absorb mainly light at the red and blue parts of the spectrum.
10	reflected and transmitted.
30.8	'lost' in the processes of photosynthesis and evaporation.
9.2	incorporated into plant products.
3.7	used up in the process of respiration

- **Gross primary productivity** (GPP) is the rate at which products are formed. A substantial amount of gross production is respired by the plant.
  Using the figures in the above table:
  GPP minus respiration = net production.
  9.2   −   3.7   =   5.5 units.

- The rate at which the products of photosynthesis accumulate is known as **net primary productivity** (NPP).
- **Secondary productivity** is the rate at which consumers accumulate energy in the form of cells or tissues.

□ *Action*   Represent the above information in the form of a flow diagram.

Biological productivity is the rate at which biomass is produced by an ecosystem.
(Biomass is the dry weight of organic matter comprising a group of organisms in a particular habitat.)
Biological productivity has two components:
1. Primary productivity – the production of new organic matter by green plants.
2. Secondary productivity - the production of new organic matter by consumers.

Herbivores have a lower secondary productivity than carnivores.

Herbivores do not eat all the vegetation in an ecosystem. Cattle grazing a field will eat the grasses and edible weeds but do not eat the roots and often leave part of the shoot system. This means that only part of the NPP of the ecosystem is transferred to the primary consumers.

Herbivores feed on plant material which contains cellulose, e.g. cows have energy consuming symbiotic microbes in their digestive tracts. Even so, their faeces contain a high proportion of undigested matter.

Carnivores have a much higher secondary productivity. This is because their protein-rich diet is more readily and efficiently digested. Only about 20% of the energy intake is lost in the faeces and urine of carnivores compared with a loss of about 66% in herbivores. Carnivores absorb almost twice as much energy per unit mass of food compared with herbivores.

❏ *Action*   1. You would be expected to answer questions involving calculations when provided with appropriate data.
2. List three strategies used by farmers to maximise productivity.

2.4 Ecological pyramids

The number of organisms, their biomass or the amount of energy contained in each trophic level can be represented in diagrams with a bar for each level. These are known as pyramids. They provide a quantitative account of the feeding relationships in a community.

Pyramids of numbers

- As you go up a food chain there is a progressive drop in the **numbers** of the organisms found at each trophic level.
- A bar diagram is drawn to indicate the relative numbers of individuals at each trophic level in a food chain.
- The overall shape is roughly that of a pyramid with the number of organisms at each level usually decreasing. This is because the loss of energy through the chain means that the higher levels can support fewer numbers and also the animals at the top tend to be larger anyway.
- There are drawbacks to the use of pyramids of numbers:
- ✓ All organisms are counted as equal, regardless of size.
- ✓ This can lead to inverted pyramids e.g. a single oak tree supporting millions of aphids.
- ✓ Juvenile or immature forms may have different energy and diet requirements to the adult.
- ✓ The numbers of some organisms may be so great that it is impossible to represent them accurately to the same scale as other species in the food chain.

Pyramids of biomass

The difficulties mentioned are partly overcome by the use of a pyramid of biomass. This reflects the decrease in **biomass** at each trophic level in a food chain. The biomass is the total weight of living matter, so it reflects both the numbers of organisms at each trophic level and also their size.

The pyramid of biomass also has its drawbacks:
- ✓ They are very time-consuming to construct.
- ✓ Since it is impossible to measure exactly the biomass of all individuals in a population, a small sample is taken.
- ✓ They can also, in certain circumstances, give rise to an inverted pyramid. E.g. at certain times of the year the biomass of zooplankton in lakes and oceans may exceed the biomass of photosynthetic phytoplankton on which they feed. This is because biomasss refers to the mass of organisms at a particular moment in time. This 'snapshot' is referred to as the **standing crop**. However, the organisms that make up the phytoplankton are smaller than the zooplankton that depend on them and have shorter life cycles. So, at any one time, the biomass of the phytoplankton may be less than the zooplankton but because the phytoplankton have a much greater turnover of numbers, over a period of time, their biomass will be greater.

Pyramids of energy

This represents the total **energy** requirement of each successive trophic level in a food chain. As material passes up through the food chain energy is lost in respiration as heat, and in excretion, so the size of the bars decreases sharply. They are usually constructed for the energy utilised by the different feeding types in a unit area over a set period of time. The use of a set period of time means that an energy pyramid overcomes the problems which arise when ecosystems are compared simply by counting or measuring the standing crop of organisms. However, obtaining the data can be complex and difficult.

❑ **Action** You should be familiar with the advantages and disadvantages of each of the three types of pyramids used in ecology.

2.4 Recycling nutrients

Although ecosystems receive an inexhaustible influx of solar energy, chemical elements are available only in limited amounts. Life therefore depends on the recycling of essential chemical elements. Microorganisms play an important role in the process of decay, releasing compounds of these elements from the bodies of dead organisms.

Carbon cycle

Carbon dioxide is added to the air by the respiration of animals, plants and microorganisms and by the combustion of fossil fuels. Photosynthesis takes place on so great a scale that it re-uses on a daily basis almost as much carbon dioxide as is released into the atmosphere. This is the basis of the carbon cycle. The production of carbohydrates, proteins and fats contributes to plant growth and subsequently to animal growth through complex food webs. The dead remains of both plants and animals are then acted upon by saprobionts in the soil which ultimately release gaseous CO_2 back to the atmosphere.

In past times large quantities of dead organisms accumulated in aerobic conditions and so were prevented from decaying. In time they formed coal, oil and other fossil fuels. The burning of these fuels returns more CO_2 to the atmosphere and has resulted in a rise in CO_2 in the atmosphere, particularly over the last 50 years.

❏ *Action*   Draw a labelled diagram of the carbon cycle linking the processes of photosynthesis, respiration, decomposition, fossilisation and combustion.

Changes in the biosphere

The biosphere is the layer of air surrounding the earth's surface.

Depletion of the ozone layer
Ozone collects naturally in the upper atmosphere and this layer forms a barrier to ultra-violet rays. Some pollutants, e.g. CFC's (chlorofluorocarbons) found in aerosols, damage the ozone layer when they are released. The ozone layer becomes thinner and 'holes' have appeared over the South pole. This results in less UV radiation being absorbed and so more reaches the earth's surface.
This has two main effects:
1.   Increased temperature i.e. global warming.
2.   Increased UV radiation, which is linked to an increase in skin cancer.

The greenhouse effect
Some pollutant gases are called 'greenhouse gases' because they form a layer in the atmosphere, which acts like glass in a greenhouse. They allow high-energy solar radiation to pass through to the earth's surface. Much of this energy is 'bounced back' towards space as heat, which greenhouse gases 'trap'. This causes **global warming**. Greenhouse gases include carbon dioxide, methane, CFC's and nitrous oxide. The amount of greenhouse gases in the environment is known to be rising.
Carbon dioxide is particularly important in the greenhouse effect because it represents about 49% of all greenhouse gases. Carbon dioxide is formed during the **respiration** of organisms and the burning of **fossil fuels.** That produced as a result of respiration is taken up by plants during photosynthesis, ensuring it does not accumulate. However, carbon dioxide concentrations in the atmosphere have increased.

There are two main reasons for the increase:
1. **The burning Fossil fuels** – accounts for about 70% of the increases in CO_2, most (76%) coming from industrialised countries.
2. **Deforestation** – accounts for about 30% of the increased CO_2 levels, with about half the world's forests having been removed over the last 30 years.
   There are three reasons for this:
   ✓ Timber removal means there are fewer trees to absorb CO_2 for photosynthesis.
   ✓ Deforestation is often accompanied by burning of remaining vegetation to prepare land for cultivation.
   ✓ Any unburnt vegetation may quickly die and decompose, releasing CO_2.
   The regrowth of vegetation after deforestation is usually insufficient to offset these effects.

Possible effects of global warming
Various predictions have been made. Possible temperature increases during the next 50 years have been suggested in the range $1.5 - 5.5°C$, if concentrations of greenhouse gases rise at current rates.
Possible effects may be:
✓ Some melting of polar icecaps would result in flooding in coastal areas.
✓ Increased frequency of droughts, hurricanes and cyclones, and also forest fires.
✓ In tropical areas of the world decreased availability of water might lead to the formation of deserts.
✓ Increased crop yields, but insect pest populations might also increase.
To date, although governments agree that there is a link between greenhouse gas concentrations and global warming they cannot agree on a reduction in levels of industrial emissions. Soon, the ecological problem will be too big to solve.

Nitrogen cycle

The nitrogen cycle is the flow of organic and inorganic nitrogen within an ecosystem where there is an interchange between nitrogenous compounds and atmospheric nitrogen.
The main processes involved are as follows. (You are **not** required to know the specific names of the bacteria involved.)
- **Putrefaction** – decay processes convert organic nitrogen (the protein of dead organisms) into ammonia. Various bacteria and fungi carry out this process.
- **Nitrification** – the ammonia formed in putrefaction is converted by nitrification via nitrites to nitrates, the main absorbable form of nitrogen. Various bacteria are involved; e.g. ammonia is converted to nitrite (by *Nitrosomonas*) and nitrite to nitrate (by *Nitrobacter*).
- **Nitrogen fixation** – atmospheric nitrogen can be converted to nitrogen compounds by nitrogen fixation e.g. by free living bacteria (such as *Azotobacter*). There are also symbiotic nitrogen fixing bacteria (such as the bacterium *Rhizobium*) found in leguminous root nodules.
- **Denitrification** – nitrogen is lost from ecosystems by denitrification. This is a particular problem in waterlogged soils with anaerobic conditions where anaerobic bacteria (such as *Pseudomonas*) can reduce nitrates to molecular nitrogen.

✓ Nitrogen is found in all amino acids from which proteins are made. Nitrogen is available to plants only in the form of ammonium (NH_4^+) and nitrate (NO_3^-) ions and are taken up by the roots. You should link the uptake of nitrates with protein synthesis and the synthesis of nucleic acids.

- ✓ Farming practices such as ploughing and improving drainage help improve soils as these activities aerate the soil. Anaerobic bacteria cannot compete with aerobic bacteria and so denitrification does not occur.

- ❑ **Action**   Draw a labelled diagram to illustrate the processes of decay, nitrification, denitrification and nitrogen fixation.
  Make sure that you understand the nitrogen cycle. Poor responses to exam questions on this topic are common because candidates have not learnt their work.

Eutrophication and algal blooms

Eutrophication is a natural process during which the concentration of salts builds up in bodies of water.

In lakes and rivers the salts normally accumulate until an equilibrium is reached where they are exactly counterbalanced by the rate at which they are removed. The salts necessary for eutrophication of lakes and rivers are largely nitrates and phosphates. The leaching of these salts from the surrounding land is a slow, natural process. However, sewage and **fertilizers** are an additional source of these salts.

An increasing quantity of inorganic fertilizer is now applied to farmland to increase crop yield. **Nitrate** is one of the major chemicals found in fertilizers. The indiscriminate use of nitrogen-containing fertilizers may pollute water supplies and pose a threat to human health.

Nitrate is highly soluble and is readily **leached** into rivers, ponds and lakes. The first effect may be an **algal bloom**, where the waters become densely populated with species of blue-green bacteria in particular ; their growth being enhanced by abundant nutrients. At this stage the water may become green and light is unable to penetrate to any depth.

The algae in the deeper regions of the lake are therefore unable to photosynthesise, and die. The short lived blue-greens soon die and are decomposed by saprobiontic bacteria, thus creating a considerable biochemical oxygen demand (BOD). The water in all but the very upper layers becomes deoxygenated, so that fish and other oxygen-requiring species die. In the final stages of the process of eutrophication anaerobic bacteria in the water may reduce nitrate to nitrite (both nitrate and nitrite are toxic compounds). In view of their toxicity, the EU has set a limit of 11.3 parts per million (ppm) total nitrogen in drinking water. This figure has been exceeded in parts of the U.K.

2.5   Population growth

Organisms live as part of populations and communities. You should understand how factors can limit the growth of a population and how the balance between birth rate and death rate is maintained. It is possible to study the development of a community over time.

Population growth

A population is a group of organisms of a single species occupying a particular area. A typical S shaped curve of population growth traces the increase in number of a species moving into a new geographical area.

□   *Action*   Draw a generalised graph of population growth (sigmoid growth curve) with the stages of growth as shown by a liquid culture of yeast or bacteria.
Annotate the graph with the four phases described below.

- The **lag phase** – in microbes this may last from a few minutes to several days. There is little or no cell multiplication or growth. (As only a few individuals are present initially the rate of growth is very slow.) This is a period of adaptation or preparation for growth, with intense metabolic activity, notably enzyme synthesis.
- The **exponential phase** – as numbers increase, providing there is no factor limiting growth, more individuals become available for reproduction. The cells begin to divide at a constant rate. Ideally, the cell population increases geometrically. This rate of increase cannot be maintained indefinitely.
- **Stationary phase** –when birth rate of new cells is equal to the death rate of older cells population growth enters this phase. Certain factors limit the population growth. The population has reached its maximum size. This is known as the **carrying capacity** for the particular environment in which the population occurs. This describes the limit to the number of individuals that an area can support.
- **Death phase** – when death rate is greater than birth rate. This may occur when all the food in a nutrient solution has been used up.

The factors which limit the growth of a particular population are collectively called the **environmental resistance**. Such factors include available food, predation, parasitism, disease, overcrowding, competition, accumulation of toxic waste, weather.

Density dependence

You should distinguish between those factors that will slow down population growth rate and those which might cause a population crash.
- Some factors are **density dependent**, i.e. their effect increases as the density of the population increases, e.g. accumulation of toxic waste, disease, parasitism and sometimes food supply.
The carrying capacity is dependent on the resources provided for by the environment (which therefore act as density-dependent factors).
- Other factors are **density independent**, i.e. their effect does not depend on the population density; the effect is the same regardless of the size of the population. It is usually due to a sudden or violent change in an abiotic factor, e.g. freezing, flood or fires.

Regulation of population size

In general the size of a population is regulated by the balance between the birth rate and the death rate. However, populations **fluctuate**, they do not remain constant in size. However, this fluctuation is not large and erratic. The numbers of most species lie near an equilibrium point known as the **set point**. For a given species in a particular environment, there is a certain equilibrium population that the environment can support. If the population rises above the set point a density dependent factor increases mortality or reduces breeding to such an extent that the population declines.

If the population falls below the set point, environmental resistance is temporarily relieved so that the population rises again.

Two other influences on the size of a population are:
- **Immigration** – occurs when individuals join a population from neighbouring populations.
- **Emigration** – occurs when individuals depart from a population. Factors such as overcrowding may often act as a stimulus. Whereas migration is a periodic seasonal movement, emigration is a non-reversible one-way process. The size of a population may fluctuate on a regular basis. This may be the consequence of weather patterns such as temperature or rainfall.

You will be expected to
1. Plot graphs of population growth rate when provided with appropriate data.
2. Interpret graphs of changes in population growth rate.

Competition and predation

- **Competition** – individuals of a species in a population are continually competing with each other.

Plants compete for space, light and mineral ions; animals compete for food, shelter and a mate.

There are two forms of competition:
- ✓ **Intraspecific competition** occurs between individuals of the same species.
- ✓ **Interspecific competition** occurs between individuals of different species.

- A **predator** is an organism that feeds on living species. Predators are normally larger than their prey and tend to kill before they eat. The abundance of prey is a factor limiting the numbers of the predator. Within a food chain, a predator-prey relationship causes both populations to oscillate and these oscillations are regulated by the process known as **negative feedback**.

(Predator–prey relationships is also studied in an applied way in 'biological control' on pages 69–70.)

Community and succession

Ecosystems are dynamic and subject to change.

A **community** is all the plants and animals occupying a particular area.
- **Primary succession** refers to the introduction of plants/animals into areas that have not previously been colonised, e.g. bare rock.
- **Secondary succession** refers to the reintroduction of organisms into a bare habitat previously occupied by plants and animals. If the original vegetation is removed, e.g. by

fire, tree felling, the area rapidly becomes recolonised by a succession of different plants and animals.

In any area, over time, new organisms replace existing ones (species diversity increases) until a stable state is reached. All successions usually involve changes in community structure and function until a community reaches a climax of succession known as the **climax community**, e.g. a mature woodland. This is a stable community which undergoes no further change.

A series of successional stages is called a **sere**. Each seral community is called a seral stage leading to a climax community. The transition of one stage to the next is called a **succession**.

Bare rock is colonised by **algae and lichens**, forming a **pioneer community**. The accumulation of dead and decomposing organic material and the weathering of the rock leads to the formation of a primitive soil in which the higher plants can grow. **Mosses and ferns** appear and as the soil develops, **grasses**, **shrubs** and **trees** appear.

(Don't forget that the community consists of animals as well as plants and that the animals have undergone a similar series of successional stages dictated by the plant types present at each stage.

In a secondary succession, seeds, spores and organs of vegetative reproduction may remain in the soil and dispersal of plants and migration of animals will assist in colonisation of the habitat.)

❏   **Action**   Construct a flow diagram to show the colonisation of bare rock to climax community and insert key terms as appropriate.

2.6 Human activities

Humans are dependent on the earth's resources for their survival. The increase in human population has meant that more food has to be produced to support it. In agriculture an increase in land use and over-fishing of the oceans has led to a conflict between production and conservation. The use of pesticides and fertilizers have improved crop yield but environmental issues arise from their use.

Agricultural exploitation

The main purpose of agriculture is to produce food for human consumption. Both the efficiency and the intensity of food production are being continually increased to meet the demands of the human population. There are several environmental implications for this:

- **Land clearance** – for cultivation and for grazing reducing the number of potential habitats available. Tropical forests are cleared for timber and land use on a massive scale destroying important habitats and making the soil unstable. Destruction of the habitat reduces variation and hence the gene pool. This has the effect of:
  ✓ decreasing the **diversity** of species;
  ✓ making the land more exposed and vulnerable to wind. This can blow away topsoil, leading to **erosion**.
- **Monoculture** – is the simultaneous growth of large numbers of crop plants of similar age and type within a defined area. Monoculture is an 'artificial' situation because there will normally be a succession leading to a greater diversity of species If the same crop is grown on the same plot year after year yield progressively declines. This is due in part to mineral depletion but also conditions become ideal for the crop plant's pests and parasites. This is resisted in monoculture by the use of selective **herbicides** to prevent the growth of weeds, and **pesticides** to remove insect and other pests.
- **Over-production**
  Maximum use is made of available agricultural land by intensive cultivation, including the use of nitrate fertilizers. This has two possible effects:
  ✓ Soil erosion.
  ✓ Eutrophication (see page 62).

Deforestation

Forests cover about 34% of the world's land surface. However, about half the world's forests have been removed (deforestation) during the last 30 years. The sale of valuable timber, the freeing of land for alternative uses such as subsistence farming and cash crops, clearing land for roads etc, has meant that the trees of forests and woodland are being cut down faster than they can be replanted or regenerated naturally.
The consequences of deforestation are:

- **Climate change** – a reduction in the removal of CO_2 from the atmosphere as there is less global photosynthesis. This in turn may lead to global warming (see pages 60-61).
- **Soil erosion**.
  ✓ Digging and ploughing loosen the topsoil, assisting in the process of soil erosion.
  ✓ The removal of vegetation affects regional climate mainly by reducing rainfall thus accelerating desertification.
  ✓ Deforestation of the watershed causes lowland **flooding.**
  The removal of vegetation on the higher slopes of valleys results in heavy rain sweeping exposed soil to the flood plains below. On the lower slopes, plants and leaf litter would act as a sponge soaking up heavy rainfall and water would gradually be released into the

soil. Instead, due to the absence of plants, only evaporation occurs. This is generally slower than transpiration in returning water vapour to the atmosphere, so soil conditions become wetter.

- **Destruction of natural habitats**, leading to a reduction in biodiversity. It is estimated that at least 50% of the earth's species live in the tropical rain forests, even though they only occupy about 10% of the earth's land area. If natural habitats are destroyed this may lead to the loss of medicinal properties of some tropical plants that may become extinct before their clinical properties have been investigated.

Agricultural management
Possible solutions to the problem of deforestation are:
- ✓ **Managed forests** involving sustainable replanting and regeneration.
- ✓ Providing **protected areas** to preserve species.
    Efforts are being made to conserve the dwindling areas of tropical rain forests. This involves the development of habitats which are legally safeguarded and patrolled by wardens.
    Giving authorities greater powers to control developments and activities within designated areas.

Fishing

There have been dramatic increases in the intensity and efficiency of commercial fishing methods. This has resulted in **over-fishing** in many of the areas of the world. Fish are an example of a renewable resource. Over-fishing results in a depletion of younger fish, so that the 'breeding stock' is unable to maintain previous population levels. If the rate at which they are removed exceeds that at which they have been produced their supply is ultimately exhausted. Fish are not generally farmed. Humans remove them from the seas with no attempt to replace stocks by breeding.
International agreement has been reached on controls such as:
- imposing quotas.
- restricting the mesh size of nets – larger mesh nets allow juvenile fish to escape, and so survive to reproduce.
- having closed seasons for fishing.
- enforcing exclusion zones.

The European Commission has successfully banned the fishing of particular species. This measure enables the breeding stocks to recover. Legislation limiting the size of fishing fleets, restricting the numbers of days spent at sea and controlling the mesh size of nets have been less successful as they are difficult to enforce. This is because commercial fishermen naturally resist attempts to limit their income or their job prospects.

Pest control

Pests attack crop plants and animals, causing a reduction in yield. Pests:
- ✓ feed on crops and animals;
- ✓ compete with crop organisms for resources;
- ✓ can directly cause disease in crop organisms;
- ✓ can make infection by pathogens more likely;
- ✓ can spoil food when it is being stored or transported.

These factors lead to a reduced amount of food (very important in some parts of the world, where food is in short supply), and to a massive economic loss for farmers.

Pesticides are poisonous chemicals used to control organisms considered harmful to agriculture or organisms involved in disease transmission e.g. insecticides to kill insects. Ideally a pesticide should be **specific, non-persistent** and should **not accumulate** and be passed along food chains.

Organochlorine chemicals such as DDT, were persistent and remained in the environment for long periods, a property which is regarded as undesirable in a modern pesticide. The overuse of pesticides has also led to the development of **resistance** among many species of insects.

Chemical control

This involves the use of herbicides, fungicides or insecticides to kill the pests. The chemicals can be sprayed onto the crop, applied as powders or smokes in enclosed areas, sprayed onto animals or added to animal feed.

The advantages of chemical control

1. It is a very effective means of control.
2. Pests are eradicated quickly and relatively cheaply.
3. Chemicals can be applied on a small scale, e.g. to a single field.
4. Application does not require a high level of skill.

The disadvantages of chemical control

1. The chemicals are not specific and can eradicate beneficial insects, e.g. pollinating insects, such as bees; biological control agents. With the removal of the insect predators of the pest there may be a resurgence of the pest.
2. Pests may become resistant to the pesticide.
3. Pesticides contain poisonous chemicals which can enter the food chain and may kill fish, birds or mammals.
4. Chemical residues may cause harm to humans, e.g. ship dip health problems for farmers.

Pyrethroids

The ideal insecticide is a compound, effective at low dosage that kills harmful insects, yet does not harm useful insects. It should also have no environmental effects. In recent times researchers have made considerable progress in their search for such compounds. One of the current generations of insecticides is the pyrethroids, developed from the flowers of a Kenyan daisy-like plant called pyrethrum. A powder made from parts of the flower was found to be an effective insecticide. However, the effect of the natural pyrethrum was found to be short-lived, as it was rapidly broken down by strong sunlight.

By using the natural pyrethrum as a starting point, biochemists were able to develop a more potent, safer and light stable compound, suitable for insect control in field crops. If farmers spray their crops with this compound in the early morning or late evening, they do no harm to visiting bees and ladybirds.

Biological control

The effect of the predator-prey relationship in regulating populations has been exploited by humans as a method of controlling pests, i.e. biological control methods exploit natural enemies to regulate the population of pest species. A beneficial organism (the **agent**) is deployed against an undesirable one (the **target**). The aim is to reduce the pest population to a tolerable level, i.e. an **economic injury level** for a particular crop. To eradicate the pest completely could be counter-productive. This would not leave any food source for the predator, which would then die out. Should the pest re-invade at a later date it would soon increase its numbers to an economically damaging level.

The advantages of biological control
1. It is usually highly specific to one pest.
2. It can provide long-term control if population equilibrium is established.
3. Although expensive to introduce (due to research costs) it can be very cheap in the long term.
4. There is no environmental contamination.
5.   It can be used in the glasshouse situation.

The disadvantages of biological control
1. Successful examples are relatively few in number / agents are not known for most pest problems.
2. Success usually involves a high level of skill and research. This can be expensive.
3. A detailed knowledge of the life cycle is required. There is the potential for the release of exotic organisms with unknown ecological effects. (There have been examples where the predator, having eradicated the pest, has turned to an alternative food supply and has itself become a pest.)
4. A frequent input is needed to attain a population balance.
5. Apart from glasshouse pests, it is of little use to individual producers, as introduction needs to be made on a large scale.

An example of successful biological control
Whilst a glasshouse is an ideal place for growing plants it is also an ideal habitat for many different types of insect pests. Whitefly is a pest on tomatoes and cucumbers and can cause considerable economic damage to these crops. The adult fly is a small, moth-like insect about 1mm in length with a yellow body and white wings. The adult lives for about 35 days and each female can produce between 150–500 eggs. The adults and larval stages feed on the underside of leaves by sucking sap and as they feed they produce a sticky, sugary fluid. Fungi often grow in this fluid and spoil the appearance of the leaves and the fruit. This growth also reduces photosynthesis by blocking out the light.
In the absence of their natural enemies and with abundant food and warmth their populations soar. In such a situation the grower can either use insecticide spray or introduce a natural enemy. However the whitefly is now resistant to many insecticides.
The method of biological control is to introduce a parasitic wasp into the glasshouse. The female wasps, *Encarsia formosa*, lay their eggs in the whitefly larvae. When the wasp eggs hatch the minute larvae eat the whitefly larvae, from the inside. The wasps develop inside the larvae and the adult wasps emerge after three weeks by cutting holes in the cases of the dead whitefly larvae. The wasps then start the cycle all over again. Each wasp female can lay between 60–100 eggs and only one wasp egg is laid in each whitefly larva. (The life cycle of the wasp is **not** required.)

Growers can buy the parasitic wasps. They are supplied as larvae stuck on small cards which can be placed on the plants in the glasshouse.

Integrated control

Despite the development of improved pesticides such as organophosphates, and synthetic pyrethroids similar to the naturally occurring pyrethrum, it is now felt that pest control is best achieved by combining various methods. These include the use of biological control agents, producing pest-resistant crops, varying cultivation techniques and where necessary the minimal, well-targeted application of highly selective pesticides. This is known as **integrated pest management**.

The economic importance of the nitrogen cycle

If managed properly, soil is a renewable resource in which farmers can grow food. The aim is sustainable agriculture, i.e. a commitment to involving a variety of farming methods that are conservation-based, environmentally safe, and profitable.

At present, the farmers of developed nations use commercially produced fertilizers containing minerals that are either mined or prepared by industrial processes. The three mineral elements that are most commonly deficient in farm and garden soils are nitrogen, phosphorous and potassium. Consequently fertilizers are enriched with these elements.

❑ *Action*   Consider the economic importance of the nitrogen cycle in terms of food production and the cost of fertilizer application. (Link this with 2.4).